Contents

Review: Part 1

Review: Part 2

Say the name of the picture in each box. Print the letter or letters that stand for the vowel sound.

cat   bed   pig

g<u>a</u>t<u>e</u>   j<u>ee</u>p   k<u>i</u>t<u>e</u>

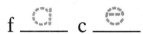 f <u>a</u> c <u>e</u>	 n ___ t	w ___ g	d ___ m ___
 b ___ k ___	 c ___ p	 s ___ ds	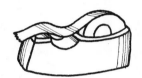 t ___ p ___
 f ___ n	 m ___ c ___	 v ___ s ___	 sh ___ p
 p ___ n	 f ___ t	 w ___ b	 p ___ p ___

Name _____

review

Find the word in the box that completes each sentence. Then print the word.

fill	race	belt	seed	vine

1. The two girls ran in a _____ race _____.

2. She is wearing a brown _____.

3. A _____ is a kind of plant.

4. A flower will grow if you plant this _____.

5. Let's _____ the jar with water.

---

eggs	size	deep	stamp	hid

6. You need a _____ for this letter.

7. The rabbit _____ in the woods.

8. What _____ shoe do you wear?

9. He is swimming in _____ water.

10. We had _____ for breakfast.

Phonics Home Activity: Ask your child to read the completed sentences on this page. Then, on another sheet of paper, help your child write the words *vine, deep,* and *hid* without looking at them.

Say the name of the picture in each box. Print the
letter or letters that stand for the vowel sound.

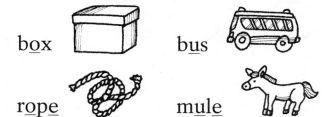

box   bus

rope   mule

gl ___ b ___   c ___ b ___   r ___ ck   s ___ n

dr ___ m   b ___ n ___   d ___ ll   m ___ l ___

st ___ v ___   tr ___ ck   h ___ s ___   sm ___ k ___

cl ___ ck   br ___ sh   r ___ b ___   r ___ s ___

Name _____   3

review

Find the word in the box that completes each sentence. Then print the word.

blocks	cute	stove	mule	drums

1. The little rabbit is ___cute___ .

2. We made a house with _____ .

3. I put the pan on the _____ .

4. He likes to play the _____ .

5. That animal is a _____ .

---

chop	cubes	broke	hum	joke

6. I can't sing, so I just _____ .

7. Mr. Lee likes to _____ wood.

8. The glass fell and _____ .

9. We laughed at the _____ she told.

10. I will cut the bread into _____ .

4 **Phonics Home Activity:** Ask your child to read the completed sentences on this page. Then, on another sheet of paper, help your child list words that rhyme with *block* (*sock, lock, rock*) and words that rhyme with *chop* (hop, mop, top).

Circle the word that names the picture. Then print the word.

pail	
(penny)	
pay	
penny	

boot
bay
bait

_____

tree
try
tray

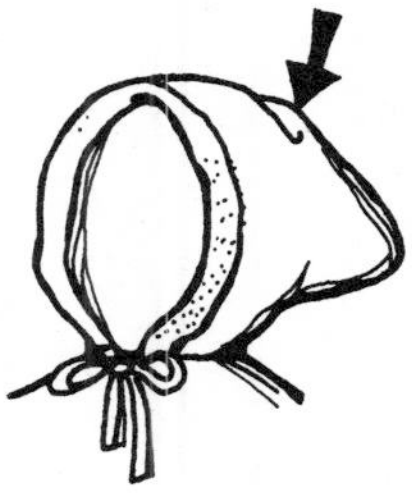

_____

hay
hood
hail

_____

main
men
moon

_____

sail
stay
stool

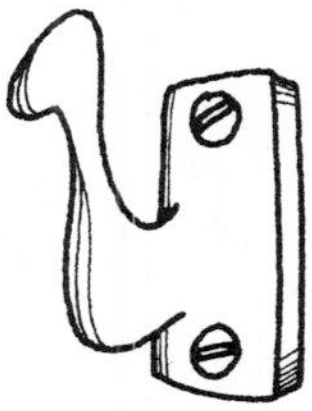

_____

hay
hook
hope

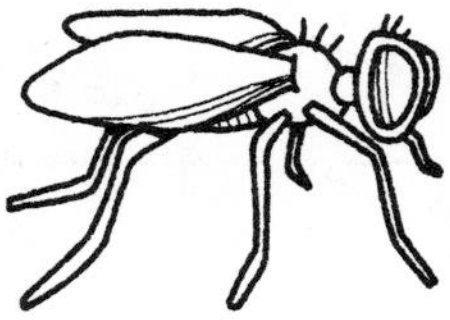

_____

fool
fly
fail

_____

pay
pool
pony

_____

hoop
hay
hail

_____

noodle
nail
nap

_____

bay
baby
bait

_____

Name _____ 5

review

Find the word in the box that completes each sentence. Then print the word.

stool	cry	stay	brains	wool

1. The child fell and started to _____cry_____ .

2. Mindy sat on the _____ .

3. We will _____ at home tonight.

4. Many people wear coats made of _____ .

5. We use our _____ to think.

---

pay	trail	noon	fry	sixty

6. We need money to _____ for this.

7. We ate lunch at _____ .

8. She walked on the _____ .

9. There were _____ people at the game.

10. We will _____ the fish for supper.

Phonics Home Activity: Ask your child to read the completed sentences on this page. Then, on another sheet of paper, help your child write the words *stay, trail,* and *noon* without looking at them.

Circle the word that names the picture. Then print the word.

jest (jewel) jolt *jewel* _____	sap seat soap _____	bee bow bay _____
leaf loaf low _____	eel oat owl _____	boat beat bow _____
stay stew stow _____	poach power peach _____	goat gown gain _____
thread throw threw _____	test tease toast _____	frown float feather _____

Name _____

7

review

Find the word in the box that completes each sentence. Then print the word.

coach	stew	shower	dreamed	ready

1. We had a rain  shower _____ this morning.

2. Last night, Al _____ about dinosaurs.

3. The _____ wants us to win the game.

4. Are you _____ to go right now?

5. Mother made a _____ for supper.

---

toads	flown	heavy	few	neat

6. This box is too _____ to move.

7. Jo keeps her room _____ .

8. We have only a _____ sandwiches left.

9. All the birds have _____ away.

10. Frogs look somewhat like _____ .

Phonics Home Activity: Ask your child to read the completed sentences on this page. Then, on another sheet of paper, help your child list words that rhyme with *stew* (few, knew, chew) and words that rhyme with *neat* (heat, meat, seat).

Circle the word that names the picture. Then print the word.

ranch (wrench) wreck _wrench_	slope sore score _____	blast glass gas _____
knee cheek need _____	tag tax tack _____	nine knife glide _____
puzzle puddle knuckle _____	rest knit wrist _____	side slide glide _____
slipper zipper sip _____	check chest wreck _____	slant scarf glaze _____

Name _____

Find the word in the box that completes each sentence. Then print the word.

| knitting | black | scoop | blanket | buzzer |

1. I can't find my ___knitting___ needles.

2. She is wearing _____ shoes.

3. He will _____ out some flour.

4. I put a _____ on the bed.

5. Push the _____ and I'll let you in.

| zebra | written | sly | knock | glad |

6. The _____ is an animal.

7. Have you _____ a letter to Grandpa?

8. We read a story about a _____ fox.

9. Please _____ first, and then go in.

10. I was _____ to hear the good news.

Phonics Home Activity: Ask your child to read the completed sentences on this page. Then, on another sheet of paper, help your child write the words *black, scoop,* and *knock* without looking at them.

Fill in the circle next to the word that names the picture.

★
● jewel
○ jail
○ jell

1.
○ mice
○ moose
○ mail

2.
○ blot
○ slot
○ knot

3.
○ flew
○ fly
○ flee

4.
○ mole
○ meal
○ mule

5.
○ teeth
○ wreath
○ knee

6.
○ chin
○ cheek
○ chain

7.
○ gate
○ got
○ goat

8.
○ zoo
○ too
○ moo

9.
○ scale
○ stale
○ snail

10.
○ lost
○ lock
○ lot

11.
○ cot
○ coat
○ cow

12.
○ tree
○ tray
○ trip

13.
○ bow
○ bee
○ boo

14.
○ loaf
○ leaf
○ life

©

Number right _____

Name _____

11

check

Fill in the circle next to the word that completes each sentence.

★ If it is not tight, it is _____ .

   ○ lease   ● loose   ○ lays

1. We ate bread and _____ for supper.

   ○ stay   ○ stow   ○ stew

2. We saw the skaters _____ by.

   ○ blame   ○ glide   ○ slice

3. If you cut your foot, it will _____ .

   ○ bleed   ○ glad   ○ slid

4. We played games at the _____ .

   ○ pry   ○ penny   ○ party

5. Many fish swim in the _____ .

   ○ brook   ○ brick   ○ brake

6. You should try not to _____ and fall.

   ○ scamp   ○ blimp   ○ slip

7. It's fun to do games and _____ .

   ○ puzzles   ○ puddles   ○ pulls

Number right _____

Phonics Home Activity: Ask your child to read the completed sentences on this page. Then help your child write the words *glide, stew,* and *brook* without looking at them.

Say each picture name. Put the letters in the right order. Then print the word.

$\underline{\text{c}}$ $\underline{\text{a}}$ $\underline{\text{t}}$

pma 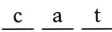 m a p	gba — — —	afn — — —
hma — — —	npa — — —	avn — — —
ckta — — — —	mpla — — — —	mta — — —
gfal — — — —	ptha — — — —	pmtsa — — — — —

Name _____

13

Read each sentence. Circle the picture that goes with it. Then print the underlined word.

1. This needs a little <u>tap</u>.

   tap

2. Where is the <u>bag</u>?

   _____

3. Bill took a <u>nap</u>.

   _____

4. Here is the <u>path</u>.

   _____

5. I will use this <u>pan</u>.

   _____

6. The hat is on the <u>rack</u>.

   _____

Phonics Home Activity: Ask your child to read each sentence and point to the picture of the underlined word. Then ask your child to write one or two of the underlined words without looking at them.

Say each picture name. Put the letters in the right order. Then print the word.

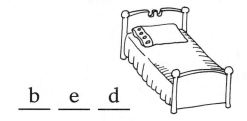

b   e   d

bwe w e b	tne ___ ___ ___	gle ___ ___ ___
etn ___ ___ ___	kcne ___ ___ ___ ___	tje ___ ___ ___
etbl ___ ___ ___ ___	tvse ___ ___ ___ ___	dsel ___ ___ ___ ___
tnte ___ ___ ___ ___	ntce ___ ___ ___ ___	nste ___ ___ ___ ___

short vowel sounds (CVC)

Read each sentence. Circle the picture that goes with it. Then print the underlined word.

1. I see the <u>chest</u>.

   __chest__

2. Here is the <u>bell</u>.

   _____

3. The <u>pen</u> is over here.

   _____

4. Let's go on the <u>sled</u>.

   _____

  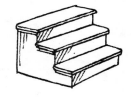

5. It's in the <u>web</u>.

   _____

6. Where is the <u>belt</u>?

   _____

16 **Phonics Home Activity:** Ask your child to read each sentence on the page, point to the correct picture, and explain why the other two pictures are not correct. Then, on a separate sheet of paper, have your child write and illustrate two of the underlined words.

Say each picture name. Put the letters in the right order. Then print the word.

p   i   g

pni

p i n

igw

_ _ _

xsi

_ _ _

fgti

_ _ _ _

kcrbi

_ _ _ _ _

phsi

_ _ _ _

tskci

_ _ _ _

lpsi

_ _ _ _

hsdi

_ _ _ _

kirtc

_ _ _ _

iklm

_ _ _ _

kcich

_ _ _ _

Name _____

Read each sentence. Circle the picture that goes
with it. Then print the underlined word.

1. Where is the <u>mitt</u>?
   _____mitt_____

2. Did you see the <u>trick</u>?
   _____

3. The <u>ship</u> is out there.
   _____

4. Here is a <u>pin</u>.
   _____

5. We got the <u>milk</u>.
   _____

6. There are <u>six</u> of us.
   _____

Phonics Home Activity: Ask your child to read each sentence and point to the picture he or she chose. Then,
on another sheet of paper, have your child copy and illustrate two of the underlined words.

Say each picture name. Put the letters in the right order. Then print the word.

b   o   x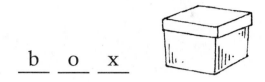

bnko k n o b	omp _ _ _	otp _ _ _
cto _ _ _	kclo _ _ _ _	otd _ _ _
ckso _ _ _ _	hpso _ _ _ _	kcro _ _ _ _
lkbco _ _ _ _ _	onkt _ _ _ _	ckclo _ _ _ _ _

Name _____ **19**

short vowel sounds (CVC)

Read each sentence. Circle the picture that goes with it. Then print the underlined word.

1. Here is your <u>cot</u>.

   cot

 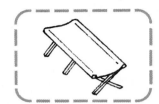 

2. She has a <u>doll</u>.

   _____

3. We used a <u>mop</u>.

   _____

4. He put on his new <u>socks</u>.

   _____

5. That is a little <u>shop</u>.

   _____

6. That's a big <u>pot</u>.

   _____

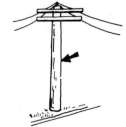  

20 **Phonics Home Activity:** Ask your child to read each sentence and point to the correct picture. Then help your child write a sentence using two of the underlined words. (For example: *The <u>doll</u> is on the <u>cot</u>.*)

Say each picture name. Put the letters in the right order. Then print the word.

b   u   s

nsu	pcu	ntu
s u n	_ _ _	_ _ _
 rgu	utb	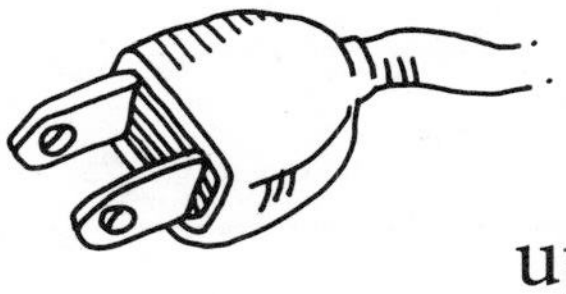 uplg
_ _ _	_ _ _	_ _ _ _
 ubc	 ubg	 pmul
_ _ _	_ _ _	_ _ _ _
 rtkcu	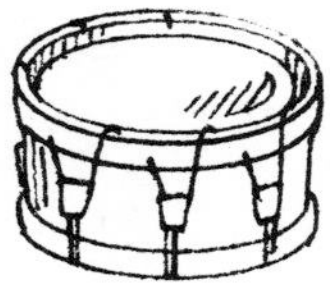 rdmu	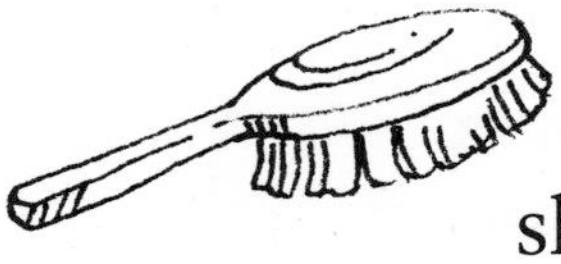 shbru
_ _ _ _ _	_ _ _ _	_ _ _ _ _

Name _____

Read each sentence. Circle the picture that goes with it. Then print the underlined word.

1. There's only one <u>nut</u> left.

nut

2. A <u>bug</u> is on the rock.

3. We need one more <u>cup</u>.

4. We put the <u>rug</u> down.

5. He will eat the <u>bun</u>.

6. There's water in the <u>tub</u>.

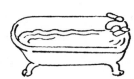 

Phonics Home Activity: Ask your child to read each sentence and point to the picture of the underlined word. Then ask your child to write one or two of the underlined words without looking at them.

Say each picture name. Fill in the circle next to the word that names the picture.

★
- ○ tuck
- ○ tick
- ● tack

1.
- ○ pan
- ○ pin
- ○ pond

2.
- ○ web
- ○ wag
- ○ wit

3.
- ○ not
- ○ net
- ○ nut

4.
- ○ fin
- ○ fan
- ○ fond

5.
- ○ pit
- ○ pat
- ○ pot

6.
- ○ lack
- ○ luck
- ○ lock

7.
- ○ ring
- ○ rang
- ○ rung

8.
- ○ sled
- ○ slid
- ○ slam

9.
- ○ bag
- ○ beg
- ○ bug

10.
- ○ jet
- ○ jot
- ○ jut

11.
- ○ met
- ○ mat
- ○ mitt

Number right _____

Name _____ 23

check

Fill in the circle next to the word that completes each sentence.

★ Beth wished her friend good _____.
- ○ lack
- ● luck
- ○ lock

1. Ben got dirty when he fell into the _____.
- ○ mad
- ○ mend
- ○ mud

2. A _____ of people were at the game.
- ○ lot
- ○ lit
- ○ lent

3. Pat _____ the hungry dogs.
- ○ find
- ○ fed
- ○ fad

4. Fran ate a _____ sandwich.
- ○ hum
- ○ hem
- ○ ham

5. Bill put the plant in a _____.
- ○ pot
- ○ pat
- ○ pest

6. My old shoes do not _____ anymore.
- ○ fat
- ○ fret
- ○ fit

7. We _____ our new teacher today.
- ○ mitt
- ○ met
- ○ mat

8. We made a _____ of things to get at the store.
- ○ list
- ○ last
- ○ lost

Number right _____ ©

24 **Phonics Home Activity:** Ask your child to read the completed sentences on this page. Then have your child choose two of the sentences to copy and illustrate on another sheet of paper.

Say each picture name. Print *qu* if the picture name
begins with the sounds for *qu*.

queen

Print *squ* if the picture name begins with the
sounds for *squ*.

squirrel

Name _____

25

qu/squ

Read each sentence. Circle the picture that goes with it. Then print the underlined word.

1. The sun makes him <u>squint</u>.

   <u>squint</u>

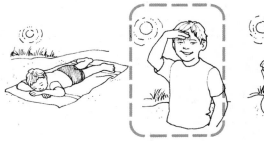

2. Here is a picture of the <u>queen</u>.

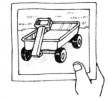  

3. She will <u>squeeze</u> it.

4. We had a <u>quiz</u> today.

5. This is a <u>square</u>.

6. There is a <u>quilt</u> on it.

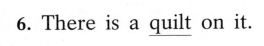  

Phonics Home Activity: Ask your child to read each sentence on the page, point to the correct picture, and explain why the other two pictures are not correct. Then, on a separate sheet of paper, have your child write and illustrate two of the underlined words.

Circle the word that completes each sentence. Then print the word.

★ When I take your picture, try not to

_____squint_____ .

quiet   (squint)   quiz

1. There is a _____ on Jan's bed.

quick   quilt   quake

2. Lee did not _____ the game.

squish   quiz   quit

3. The opposite of *slow* is _____ .

quick   quack   squeak

4. The table is _____ .

quake   quilt   square

5. We should be _____ in the library.

quilt   quiet   squeal

6. If you walk on the hat, you will _____ it.

squash   squeal   quake

Name _____ 27

check Say each picture name. Fill in the circle if the picture name begins with the sounds for *qu*.

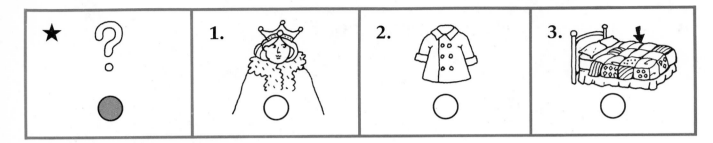

| ★ ? ● | 1. ○ | 2. ○ | 3. ○ |

Fill in the circle if the picture name begins with the sounds for <u>squ</u>.

| ★ ● | 4. ○ | 5. ○ | 6. ○ |

Fill in the circle next to the word that completes each sentence.

★ We heard the little pigs _____ .
　○ square　　● squeal　　○ quarter

7. We had a _____ in school today.
　○ squawk　　○ quit　　○ quiz

8. The box is _____ .
　○ quilt　　○ square　　○ squeal

9. We made a _____ for the bed.
　○ squeeze　　○ quake　　○ quilt

10. Let's _____ the oranges to make juice.
　○ squint　　○ quiz　　○ squeeze

Number right _____

Phonics Home Activity: Have your child tell which picture names in the first section have the sounds for *qu* and which picture names in the second section have the sounds for *squ*. Then ask your child to read the completed sentences at the bottom of the page.

28

Say each picture name. Circle each picture whose
name has the sound for g that you hear in *game*.

game

Circle each picture whose name has the sound for g
that you hear in *giraffe* and *page*.

giraffe   page

Name _____

g/j/

Say each picture name. Circle the g and the letter that follows it in the name. Print the name in the correct column.

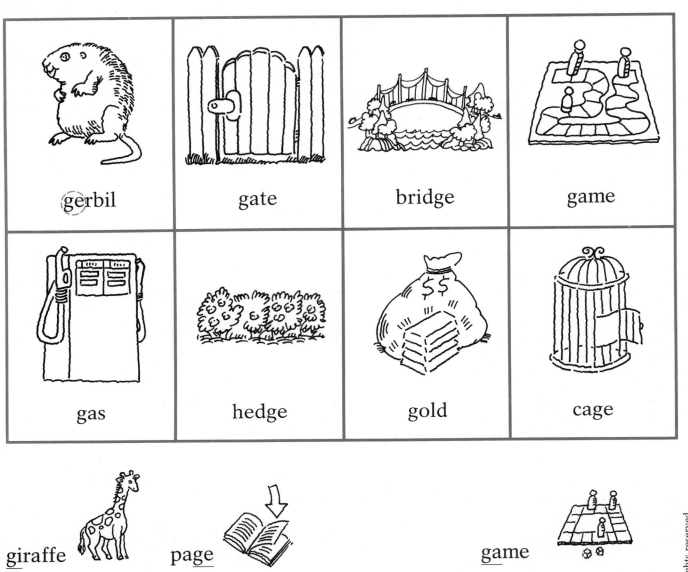

gerbil   gate   bridge   game

gas   hedge   gold   cage

giraffe   page

gerbil

game

gate

Phonics Home Activity: Ask your child to read the word in each box and to tell what letter follows the *g* in the word. Then help your child read the words he or she wrote at the bottom of the page.

Read the sentences and look at the pictures. Print
A next to the sentence that tells about Picture A.
Print B next to the sentence that tells about Picture B.

He is selling games. A

He is selling gems. B

 A.  B.

The car is on the bridge. _____

The car needs gas. _____

 A.  B.

Here is the judge. _____

Here is the jug. _____

 A.  B.

The plant is on the gate. _____

The plant is on the ledge. _____

 A.  B.

This story is about a giant. _____

© This story is about a goldfish. _____

 A.  B.

Name _____ 31

Say each picture name. Fill in the circle if the picture name has the sound for *g* that you hear in *giraffe* and *page*.

★ (●)	1. ○	2. ○	3. ○
4. ○	5. ○	6. ○	7. ○

Fill in the circle next to the word that completes each sentence.

★ We planted a _____ around our house.
   ○ huge   ● hedge   ○ hog

8. She has a _____ for her pet rabbit.
   ○ budge   ○ cage   ○ gather

9. The captain wears a special _____ on his shirt.
   ○ gasp   ○ stage   ○ badge

10. We will watch the play on the _____ .
    ○ gum   ○ judge   ○ stage

11. The bus will drive over the _____ .
    ○ bridge   ○ brick   ○ ginger

Number right _____ ©

32 **Phonics Home Activity:** Have your child name each picture in the top section of this page and tell whether it contains the sound for *g* that you hear in *giraffe* and *page.* Then ask your child to read the completed sentences at the bottom of the page.

Say each picture name. Print <u>thr</u> if the picture name begins with the sounds for <u>thr</u>.

three

thr _____ _____ _____

Print <u>str</u> if the picture name begins with the sounds for <u>str</u>.

<u>str</u>awberry

str _____ _____ _____

Print <u>spr</u> if the picture name begins with the sounds for <u>spr</u>.

<u>spr</u>ing

spr _____ _____ _____

Name _____ 33

thr/str/spr

Read each sentence. Circle the picture that goes with it. Then print the underlined word.

1. Ken is <u>spraying</u> the water.

   spraying

2. Miss Jones is using a <u>straw</u>.

   _____

3. The bed has a <u>spread</u> on it.

   _____

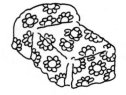  

4. He is on a <u>throne</u>.

   _____

5. Tina has the <u>thread</u>.

   _____

6. Here is the <u>stroller</u>.

   _____

Houghton Mifflin Company. All rights reserved.

Phonics Home Activity: Ask your child to read each sentence and point to the picture he or she chose. Then, on another sheet of paper, have your child copy and illustrate two of the underlined words.

Circle the word that completes each sentence.
Then print the word.

1. Tara's shirt has red and white _____ stripes _____ .

   sprint   throws   (stripes)

2. Mel is not well. His _____ hurts.

   sprout   throat   strut

3. We will _____ some water on the garden.

   spray   stray   throat

4. Al likes to eat _____ .

   sprains   thrones   strawberries

5. Please _____ the cheese on this bread.

   spread   struck   thread

6. In baseball, you are out if you get three _____ .

   throats   strikes   sprouts

7. I saw a fish in the _____ .

   spread   stream   throw

8. He will make my coat with cloth and _____ .

   thread   stroller   sprinkler

Name _____   35

Say each picture name. Fill in the circle next to the letters that stand for the beginning sounds.

★	1.	2.	3.
● str	○ str	○ spr	○ str
○ spr	○ spr	○ str	○ spr
○ thr	○ thr	○ thr	○ thr

4.	5.	6.	7.
○ str	○ thr	○ str	○ str
○ spr	○ spr	○ spr	○ thr
○ thr	○ str	○ thr	○ spr

Fill in the circle next to the word that completes each sentence.

★ I've never ＿＿＿ such a heavy ball before.

○ strap   ● thrown   ○ spread

8. There are many kinds of fish in that ＿＿＿ .

○ stream   ○ thrill   ○ sprain

9. We will ＿＿＿ water on the flowers to make them grow.

○ throat   ○ spray   ○ stripe

10. Les used a needle and ＿＿＿ to fix it.

○ sprout   ○ spray   ○ thread

Number right ＿＿＿ ©

36 **Phonics Home Activity:** Hold this page where your child can't see it, and name each picture. Ask your child to tell whether the picture name contains the sounds for *thr, str,* or *spr.* Then have your child read the completed sentences at the bottom of the page.

Say each picture name. Put the letters in the right order. Then print the word.

g   a   t   e

vwea w a v e	aerc _ _ _ _	cgae _ _ _ _
vsae _ _ _ _	veca _ _ _ _	akre _ _ _ _
etga _ _ _ _	enac _ _ _ _	epta _ _ _ _
cpae _ _ _ _	elka _ _ _ _	mgea _ _ _ _

Read each sentence. Circle the picture that goes with it. Then print the underlined word.

1. This is a <u>vase</u>.

___vase___

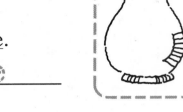

2. Ann has a <u>cape</u>.

_____

3. He will <u>tape</u> it.

_____

4. Here is the <u>cane</u>.

_____

5. The <u>rake</u> is out here.

_____

Phonics Home Activity: Ask your child to read each sentence and point to the correct picture. Then help your child write a sentence using two of the underlined words. (For example: *The <u>tape</u> is next to the <u>vase</u>.*)

Say each picture name. Put the letters in the right order. Then print the word.

k i t e

pnei p i n e	beki _ _ _ _	neni _ _ _ _
dvei _ _ _ _	cmie _ _ _ _	vnie _ _ _ _
rdei _ _ _ _	efvi _ _ _ _	dmei _ _ _ _
eppi _ _ _ _	lnei _ _ _ _	evhi _ _ _ _

Name _____

39

long vowel sounds (CVCe)

Read each sentence. Circle the picture that goes with it. Then print the underlined word.

1. He showed me the <u>vine</u>.

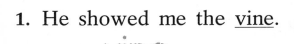

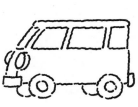  

2. There is a <u>pine</u>.

_____

3. I'll take this <u>pile</u>.

_____

4. This is my <u>kite</u>.

_____

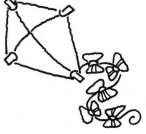  

5. The <u>knife</u> is in here.

_____

  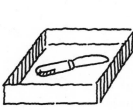

Phonics Home Activity: Ask your child to read each sentence and point to the picture of the underlined word. Then ask your child to write one or two of the underlined words without looking at them.

Say each picture name. Put the letters in the right order. Then print the word.

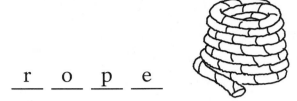

r o p e

etno

n o t e

ocne

____

ebro

____

sreo

____

ehlo

____

sneo

____

onbe

____

ohse

____

eplo

____

Name _____

long vowel sounds (CVCe)

Read each sentence. Circle the picture that goes with it. Then print the underlined word.

1. Here is the <u>code</u>.

   code

2. This is a <u>cone</u>.

   _____

3. He is on the <u>pole</u>.

   _____

4. Do you see the <u>bone</u>?

   _____

5. The bird is on the <u>stone</u>.

   _____

6. There is the <u>robe</u>.

   _____

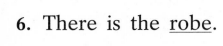

Phonics Home Activity: Ask your child to read each sentence on the page, point to the correct picture, and explain why the other two pictures are not correct. Then, on a separate sheet of paper, have your child write and illustrate two of the underlined words.

Each sentence tells about a word with the long *u* sound. Put the letters of the word in the right order. Then print the word.

1. This word names something you may want to put in your juice.

b u e c   <u>c u b e</u>

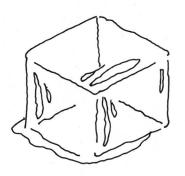

2. This word means "very big."

e g u h   ___ ___ ___ ___

3. This word names a hard-working animal.

m l e u   ___ ___ ___ ___

4. People often use this word when they talk about a baby or a baby animal.

t e c u   ___ ___ ___ ___

Name _____   **43**

long vowel sounds (CVCe)

Read each sentence. Circle the picture that goes with it. Then print the underlined word.

1. This picture is <u>cute</u>.

   cute

2. Would you like a <u>cube</u>?

   _____

3. Here is the <u>mule</u>.

   _____

4. This animal is <u>huge</u>.

   _____

Phonics Home Activity: Ask your child to read each sentence and point to the picture he or she chose. Then have your child cut out each circled picture and the word he or she has written. Mix up the words and pictures. Then help your child match each picture with the word that names it.

Say each picture name. Fill in the circle next to the word that names the picture.

★	● face
	○ fake
	○ fat

1. 
- ○ bit
- ○ bill
- ○ bike

2. 
- ○ cut
- ○ cute
- ○ cape

3. 
- ○ pine
- ○ pin
- ○ pile

4. 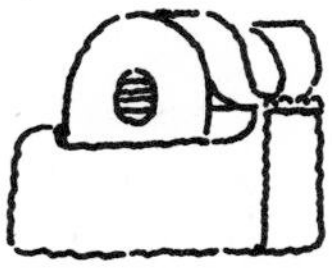
- ○ take
- ○ tape
- ○ tap

5. 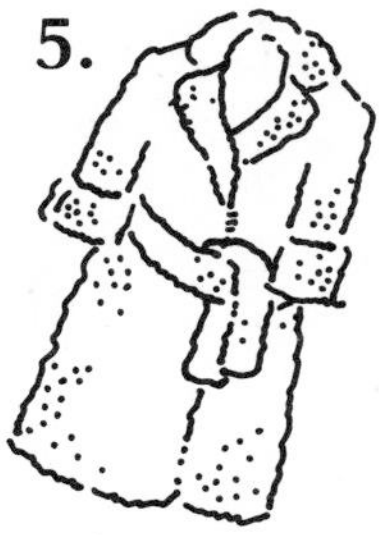
- ○ rose
- ○ rob
- ○ robe

6. 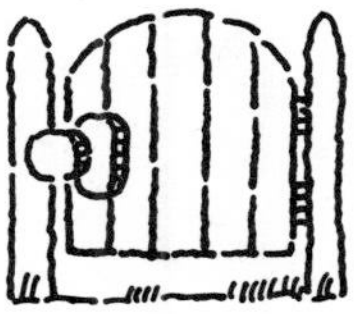
- ○ gap
- ○ game
- ○ gate

7. 
- ○ not
- ○ note
- ○ nose

8. 
- ○ cube
- ○ cute
- ○ cub

9. 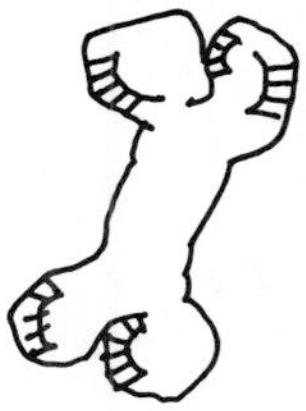
- ○ cone
- ○ bone
- ○ bond

10. 
- ○ lime
- ○ dim
- ○ dime

11. 
- ○ lack
- ○ lake
- ○ lane

©

Number right _____

Name _____

45

Fill in the circle next to the word that completes each sentence.

★ A story is sometimes called a _____.

(●) tale   ( ) tan   ( ) tall

1. Let's go for a _____ in the car.

( ) rid   ( ) ride   ( ) rope

2. Dave is wearing his new _____.

( ) rice   ( ) rob   ( ) robe

3. The fruit is _____ and very good to eat.

( ) rip   ( ) ripe   ( ) rope

4. I will write a _____ to my friend.

( ) not   ( ) name   ( ) note

5. A _____ is an animal.

( ) mush   ( ) mope   ( ) mule

6. Sally _____ on the bus today.

( ) robe   ( ) rode   ( ) rod

7. Jean had a big smile on her _____.

( ) fact   ( ) file   ( ) face

8. The little cub is very _____.

( ) cute   ( ) cut   ( ) cent

Number right _____ ©

Phonics Home Activity: Ask your child to read a few of the sentences he or she has completed. Then help your child write a sentence using two of the answer choices. (For example: *Juan wrote a tale about a mule.*)

Say each picture name. Circle each picture whose
name has the sounds for *er*, *ir*, and *ur*.

ladder    shirt    turtle

Name _____   **47**

Say each picture name. Print *er* if the picture name has the sounds for *er*.

lad<u>d</u><u>er</u>

e r _____ _____ _____

Print *ir* if the picture name has the sounds for *ir*.

sh<u>ir</u>t

i r _____ _____ _____

Print *ur* if the picture name has the sounds for *ur*.

t<u>ur</u>tle

u r _____ _____ _____

48 **Phonics Home Activity:** Help your child cut out all the pictures in the top section of this page whose names contain the sounds for *er*. Then, on another sheet of paper, have your child print the letters *er* and paste the pictures under those letters. Repeat the activity with the *ir* and *ur* sections of this page.

Circle the picture the sentence tells about. Then print the underlined word.

1. She is <u>squirting</u> water.

squirting

2. We need the <u>nurse</u>.

_____

3. He is on the <u>corner</u>.

_____

4. He drew a <u>circle</u>.

_____

5. Here is Lil's <u>purse</u>.

_____

6. She has a <u>hammer</u>.

_____

Name _____ 49

check

Say each picture name. Fill in the circle if the picture name has the sounds for *er*, *ir*, and *ur*.

Fill in the circle next to the word that completes each sentence.

★ She will wear her blue _____ .
○ third   ○ turn   ● skirt

8. Mix the flour and water and _____ them well.
○ stir   ○ germ   ○ fur

9. You should _____ or you'll be late.
○ thirsty   ○ curl   ○ hurry

10. It is very hot here in the _____ .
○ squirm   ○ summer   ○ first

Number right _____ ©

Phonics Home Activity: Ask your child to name each picture in the top section of this page and to tell whether or not the picture name contains the sounds for *er, ir,* and *ur*. Then have your child read the completed sentences and choose two of them to copy and illustrate on a separate sheet of paper.

Say each picture name. Circle each picture whose
name has the sounds for *ar*.

c<u>ar</u>

Name _____ 51

Say each picture name. Print *ar* if the picture name has the sounds for *ar*.

c<u>ar</u>

_ar_

_____ _____

_____ _____ _____

_____ _____ _____

_____ _____ _____

Phonics Home Activity: Say the name of each picture on this page, and ask your child to tell whether it contains the sounds for *ar*. Then ask your child to look in a newspaper or magazine and circle pictures of things whose names contain the sounds for *ar*.

Circle the word that completes each sentence. Then print the word.

1. We are going to ____march____ in the parade.

   starch   (march)   marsh

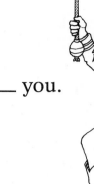

2. The dog is gentle and will not _____ you.

   harp   farm   harm

3. Our school is not _____ from here.

   tar   far   farm

4. Andy is good at drawing and all kinds of _____ .

   part   cart   art

5. Shelly put her _____ around her neck.

   scar   scarf   starch

6. The opposite of *small* is _____ .

   harm   charge   large

7. We sang and played games at the _____ .

   mark   starry   party

8. The _____ wakes me up every morning.

   alarm   tar   harm

Name _____   **53**

Say each picture name. Fill in the circle if you hear the sounds for *ar*.

| ★ (car) ⬤ | 1. ◯ | 2. ◯ | 3. ◯ |
| 4. ◯ | 5. ◯ | 6. ◯ | 7. ◯ |

Fill in the circle next to the word that completes each sentence.

★ The _____ on the wall shows different kinds of vegetables.
   ◯ start   ⬤ chart   ◯ cart

8. Last night we looked up at the _____ .
   ◯ tart   ◯ stars   ◯ scars

9. There are chickens and pigs on the _____ .
   ◯ far   ◯ cart   ◯ farm

10. This pencil has a very _____ point.
    ◯ sharp   ◯ charm   ◯ barn

11. We planted the flowers in the _____ .
    ◯ spark   ◯ garden   ◯ lark

Number right _____

Phonics Home Activity: Have your child name the pictures on this page whose names contain the sounds for *ar*. Then ask your child to read the completed sentences at the bottom of the page. Help your child list things in your home whose names contain the sounds for *ar*.

Say each picture name. Circle each picture whose
name has the sounds for *or*.

c<u>or</u>n

Name _____ **55**

Say each picture name. Print *or* if the picture name
has the sounds for *or*.

c<u>or</u>n

_or_	_____	_____
_____	_____	_____
_____	_____	_____
_____	_____	_____

Phonics Home Activity: Ask your child to name all the pictures on this page and to tell which ones contain the sounds for *or*. Then have your child cut out the pictures whose names contain the sounds for *or* and paste them onto a separate sheet of paper under the heading *or*.

Find the word in the box that completes each sentence. Then print the word.

born	corner	cord	worn

1. He has _____worn_____ those shoes every day.

2. Tie the sticks together with _____.

3. We waited at the _____ for the bus.

4. Grandpa was _____ in this house.

airport	forth	torn	forest

5. You have _____ a hole in your shirt.

6. We watched the skaters go back and_____.

7. There are many trees in the_____.

8. The plane landed at the_____.

Name _____

check

Say each picture name. Fill in the circle if you hear the sounds for *or*.

Fill in the circle next to the word that completes each sentence.

★ A _____ is a kind of bird.
  ○ storm   ○ cork   ● stork

8. You use a _____ to eat.
  ○ fork   ○ torn   ○ sort

9. Everyone sat out on the back _____.
  ○ torch   ○ pork   ○ porch

10. We had a big _____ with lots of rain.
  ○ form   ○ storm   ○ stork

Number right _____

Phonics Home Activity: Have your child read the completed sentences at the bottom of the page. Then help your child cut out all the pictures in the top section whose names contain the sounds for *or*. On another sheet of paper, have your child print *or* and paste the pictures under this heading.

58

Say each picture name. Print *ie* if you hear the
long *i* sound.

t<u>ie</u>

<u>ie</u> ___   ___   ___   ___

Print *ie* if you hear the long *e* sound.

chi<u>e</u>f

<u>ie</u> ___   ___   ___   ___

Name _____   **59**

Read each sentence. Circle the picture that goes with it. Then print the underlined word.

1. She has a <u>briefcase</u>.

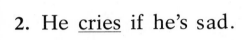

2. He <u>cries</u> if he's sad.

_____

3. This store sells <u>ties</u>.

_____

4. He cut the <u>pie</u>.

_____

5. There is a <u>collie</u>.

_____

6. This is Mr. Chan's <u>niece</u>.

_____

Phonics Home Activity: Ask your child to read each sentence and point to the correct picture. Then help your child write a sentence using two of the underlined words. (For example: *Sara's <u>niece</u> likes <u>pie</u>.*)

Circle the word that completes each
sentence. Then print the word.

1. A _____brief_____ talk doesn't last very long.

   (brief)   thief   pried

   This won't take long!

2. Dad wears a _____ to work.

   niece   necktie   thief

3. That dog is a _____.

   cried   collie   chief

4. When it doesn't rain, the pond _____ up.

   dries   fries   thief

5. Sam was tired, so he went to _____ down.

   fried   brief   lie

6. We ate chicken _____ for supper.

   pried   chief   pie

7. We cut the potato and _____ it.

   fried   flies   lied

8. Linda is Mrs. Brown's _____.

   brief   pie   niece

Name _____   61

Say each picture name. Fill in the circle if you hear the long *i* sound for *ie*.

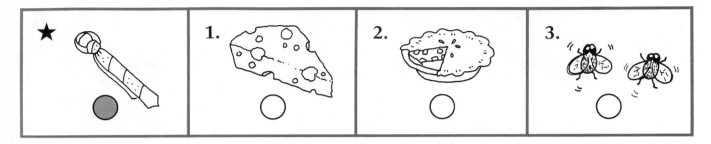

Fill in the circle if you hear the long *e* sound for *ie*.

Fill in the circle next to the word that completes
each sentence.

★ The sun _____ up the puddles of water.
   ⬤ dried   ◯ cried   ◯ field

7. I will _____ my shoelaces.
   ◯ tie   ◯ lie   ◯ niece

8. Close the windows so the _____ don't come in.
   ◯ flies   ◯ cries   ◯ fields

9. Jan _____ hard at everything she does.
   ◯ niece   ◯ tries   ◯ dies

10. When I throw the ball, my _____ runs after it.
   ◯ pie   ◯ cried   ◯ collie

Number right _____

Phonics Home Activity: Have your child color the pictures whose names contain the correct sounds in each section. Then help your child cut these pictures out and paste them on a separate sheet of paper under the heading *ie*.

Say each picture name. Print *oi* if you hear the
sound for *oi* and *oy*.

s<u>oi</u>l

oi ____   ____   ____   ____

Print *oy* if you hear the sound for *oi* and *oy*.

b<u>oy</u>

oy ____   ____   ____   ____

Name _____

oi/oy

Read each sentence. Circle the picture that goes with it. Then print the underlined word.

1. He will <u>boil</u> this.

   ___boil___

2. I used the <u>foil</u>.

   _____

   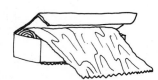 

3. She gave him a <u>toy</u>.

   _____

    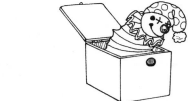 

4. He is <u>oiling</u> it.

   _____

5. This is an old <u>coin</u>.

   _____

6. Here is the <u>cowboy</u>.

   _____

     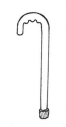

Phonics Home Activity: Ask your child to read each sentence and point to the picture of the underlined word. Then ask your child to write one or two of the underlined words without looking at them.

Circle the word that completes each sentence. Then
print the word.

1. When water gets very hot, it _____ boils _____.

   coins   joys   (boils)

2. Mom put some _____ around the food.

   foil   loyal   moist

3. A _____ is a kind of money.

   coil   point   coin

4. Dad will _____ the fish for supper.

   cowboy   broil   voice

5. You have a _____ between this book or that one.

   joy   choice   soil

6. Seth is making a _____ airplane.

   toy   toil   boil

7. We heard the good news with great _____.

   joint   toy   joy

8. Debbie has a good singing _____.

   avoid   voice   oil

check

Say each picture name. Fill in the circle if you hear the sound for *oi* and *oy*.

Fill in the circle next to the word that completes each sentence.

★ I saved _____ in a jar.
  ○ boils   ● coins   ○ joins

8. I will put my teddy bear in the _____ box.
   ○ oil   ○ foil   ○ toy

9. The plants are in the _____.
   ○ soil   ○ loyal   ○ point

10. We feel _____ when we win a game.
    ○ coil   ○ broil   ○ joy

Number right _____

Phonics Home Activity: Have your child color the pictures whose names contain the sound for *oi* and *oy*. Then help your child cut out these pictures and paste them onto a separate sheet of paper under the heading *oi* and *oy*.

Read these words. Each one ends with a vowel and *re*.

c<u>are</u>   f<u>ire</u>   m<u>ore</u>   s<u>ure</u>

Say each picture name. Circle each picture whose name ends with the sounds for *are* like *care*.

Circle each picture whose name ends with the sounds for *ire* like *fire*.

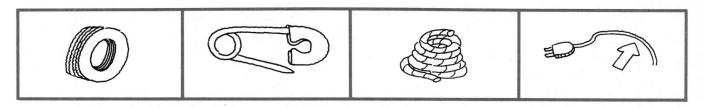

Circle each picture whose name ends with the sounds for *ore* like *more*.

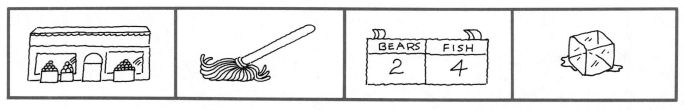

Now circle the picture that goes with the sentence below.

If you are sick, she can help find a <u>cure</u>.

Name _____   **67**

Read each meaning. Find the word in the box that goes with the meaning. Then print the word.

pure	hare	score	store	fire

1. An animal that looks like a rabbit _____hare_____

2. Something that is very hot _____

3. A place to buy things _____

4. Numbers showing the winner _____

5. Clear and with no dirt _____

shore	cure	rare	hire	fare

6. Help for one who is sick _____cure_____

7. What you pay on a bus _____

8. To give someone a job _____

9. The edge of the sea _____

10. Hard to find _____

Phonics Home Activity: Ask your child to read the completed sentences on this page. Then, on another sheet of paper, help your child list words that rhyme with *hare* (care, share, mare) and words that rhyme with *hire* (fire, tire, wire).

Circle the picture the sentence tells about. Then
print the underlined word.

1. Only the <u>core</u> is left.

   core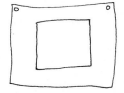

2. Beth drew a <u>square</u>.

   _____

3. Mom fixed the <u>wire</u>.

   _____

4. He is the <u>umpire</u>.

   _____

5. This water is <u>pure</u>.

   _____

6. We looked at the <u>score</u>.

   _____

Name _____

check

Say each picture name. Fill in the circle next to the letters that stand for the ending sounds.

★	○ ire ○ ore ● are	1. ○ are ○ ore ○ ire	2. ○ ore ○ ire ○ are	3. ○ ore ○ are ○ ire
4.	○ ore ○ ire ○ are	5. ○ ore ○ ire ○ are	6. ○ are ○ ore ○ ire	7. ○ ire ○ are ○ ore

Fill in the circle next to the word that completes each sentence.

★ My grandfather is going to _____ from his job.
  ● retire   ○ beware   ○ ignore

8. Miss Willet will _____ Alex to work for her.
  ○ hare   ○ hire   ○ horse

9. If you are sick, a doctor may have a _____ .
  ○ cure   ○ core   ○ curb

10. Lisa still feels a little _____ from her fall.
  ○ sir   ○ stare   ○ sore

11. When the leaves fall off, the tree is _____ .
  ○ bare   ○ bore   ○ bar

Number right _____ ©

Phonics Home Activity: Ask your child to name all the pictures on this page and to tell whether they end with the sounds for *ire*, *ore*, or *are*. Then have your child read the completed sentences at the bottom of the page.

Read each sentence. Circle the picture that goes
with it. Then print the underlined word.

find    night

1. This light is very <u>bright</u>.

___bright___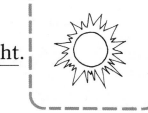

2. Laurie is trying to <u>find</u> her book.

_____

3. My dog is standing on its <u>hind</u> legs.

_____

4. Dad is on that <u>flight</u>.

_____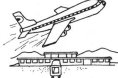

5. She is going to <u>wind</u> it.

_____

Name _____   71

ind/ight

Read each meaning. Find the word in the box that goes with the meaning. Then print the word.

kind	mind	behind	blind

1. In back of ____behind____

2. Not able to see _____

3. Thoughtful of others _____

4. What you use to think _____

---

night	flight	light	right

5. What the sun gives us _____

6. The opposite of *day* _____

7. The opposite of *left* _____

8. What you go on in an airplane _____

Phonics Home Activity: Ask your child to read the completed sentences on this page. Then, on another sheet of paper, help your child write the words *mind, light,* and *night* without looking at them.

Make each sentence tell about the picture. Circle the word you would use. Then print it.

1. He took the _____rind_____ off the orange.

   (rind)   rice   sight

2. The _____ is leaving now.

   fine   fly   flight

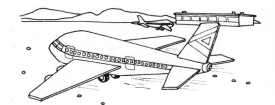

3. He wears glasses to help his _____.

   sight   slice   remind

4. I hope they won't _____!

   fit   file   fight

5. This note will _____ you.

   remind   rind   behind

6. Would you _____ helping me?

   rind   mind   find

Houghton Mifflin Company. All rights reserved.

©

Name _____

73

Read each sentence. Fill in the circle under the picture the sentence tells about.

★ She is <u>behind</u> the tree. ○ ○ ●

1. The <u>flight</u> left on time. ○ ○ ○

2. This is too <u>tight</u>. ○ ○ ○

3. He will <u>wind</u> it all up. ○ ○ ○

Fill in the circle next to the word that completes each sentence.

★ Judy likes to wear _____ colors.
○ blind   ● bright   ○ bite

4. We will turn _____ to get to my house.
○ rind   ○ right   ○ night

5. I'm calling to _____ you about our meeting.
○ remind   ○ ripe   ○ slight

6. It's time to _____ my watch.
○ wind   ○ win   ○ wife

Number right _____

74 **Phonics Home Activity:** Ask your child to read sentences in the top section and to point to the picture he or she chose. Then have your child read the completed sentences at the bottom of the page.

Read each sentence. Circle the picture that goes
with it. Then print the underlined word.

photo    elephant

1. You play music on a phonograph.

   __phonograph__

2. You can talk on a telephone.

   _____

3. Who could be a nephew?

   _____

4. A microphone helps others hear you.

   _____

5. Henry is making a photocopy.

   _____

Name _____

ph

Circle the word that names the picture. Then print the word.

phonograph

phone

(photographer)

photographer

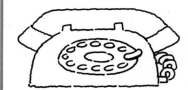
television

telegraph

telephone

_____

trophy

treaty

telephone

_____

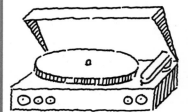
phone

phonograph

nephew

_____

phone

microphone

photograph

_____

nephew

elephant

photocopy

_____

microscope

microphone

nephew

_____

nephew

alphabet

photocopy

_____

Phonics Home Activity: Have your child cut out each picture and the word he or she has written. Mix up the words and pictures. Then help your child match each picture with the word that names it.

Circle the word that completes each sentence. Then print the word.

1. We listened to music on the ___phonograph___.

   elephant   (phonograph)   photocopy

2. My little sister can say the _____.

   nephew   trophy   alphabet

3. An _____ is a huge animal.

   elephant   alphabet   phone

4. Your _____ is ringing.

   photo   phone   trophy

5. Barry sang into the _____.

   trophy   alphabet   microphone

6. We hope our team will win the _____.

   trophy   alphabet   telegraph

7. Fred is Miss Gregory's _____.

   photocopy   telephone   nephew

8. Peter's mother is a _____ for the paper.

   photographer   phone   microphone

Say each picture name. Fill in the circle if you hear the sound for *ph* in the word. The sound can be at the beginning, middle, or end.

Fill in the circle next to the word that completes each sentence.

★ May I put the record on the _____ ?
○ nephew   ○ phone   ● phonograph

8. We saw some _____ at the zoo.
○ elephants   ○ phonographs   ○ photos

9. Grandmother called me on the _____ .
○ photograph   ○ telephone   ○ nephew

10. Hollie wrote all the letters of the _____ .
○ alphabet   ○ microphone   ○ photo

11. Phil is a _____ of Miss Harvey's.
○ trophy   ○ phone   ○ nephew   Number right _____ ©

Phonics Home Activity: Ask your child to name each picture in the top section of this page and to tell whether or not the picture name contains the sound for *ph*. Then have your child read the completed sentences and choose two of them to copy and illustrate on a separate sheet of paper.

Say each picture name. Print *ng* if you hear the
sounds for *ng* at the end of the word.

ng/nk

swing

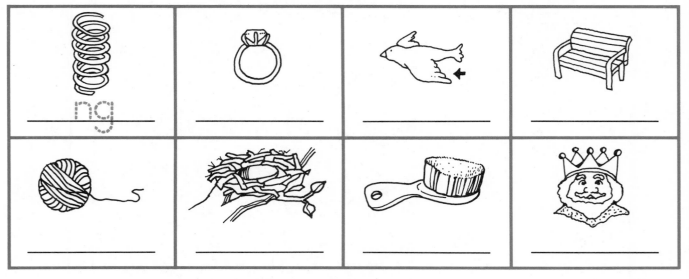

ng _____ _____ _____ _____

_____ _____ _____ _____

Print *nk* if you hear the sounds for *nk* at the end.

sku<u>nk</u>

nk _____ _____ _____ _____

_____ _____ _____ _____

ng/nk

Read each sentence. Circle the picture that goes with it. Then print the underlined word.

1. That's a big <u>chunk</u>.

   chunk

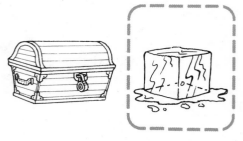

2. Here is the <u>wing</u>.

   _____

3. My money is in a <u>bank</u>.

   _____

  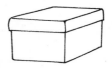

4. The boy is <u>winking</u>.

   _____

5. His arm is in a <u>sling</u>.

   _____

6. She will <u>wring</u> it out.

   _____

Phonics Home Activity: Ask your child to read each sentence on the page, point to the correct picture, and explain why the other two pictures are not correct. Then, on a separate sheet of paper, have your child write and illustrate two of the underlined words.

Read the sentences and look at the pictures. Print
A next to the sentence that tells about Picture **A**.
Print **B** next to the sentence that tells about Picture **B**.

This <u>sank</u> into the pond. _B_
This closed with a <u>bang</u>. _A_

A.

B.

Look at all this <u>junk</u>! _____
Look! I've just been <u>stung</u>! _____

A.

B.

She is at the skating <u>rink</u>. _____
She has her arm in a <u>sling</u>. _____

A.

B.

This shirt has really <u>shrunk</u>! _____
This shirt has been <u>hung</u> up. _____

A.

B.

This page is <u>blank</u>. _____
© This page shows what we <u>sang</u>. _____

A.

B.

Name _____

Say each picture name. Fill in the circle if you hear the sounds for *ng* at the end of the word.

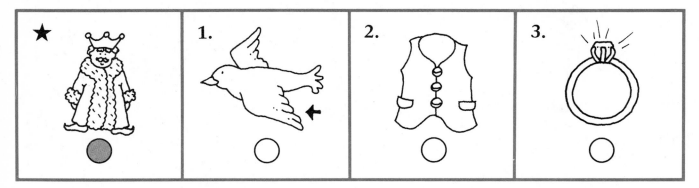

Fill in the circle if you hear the sounds for *nk* at the end of the word.

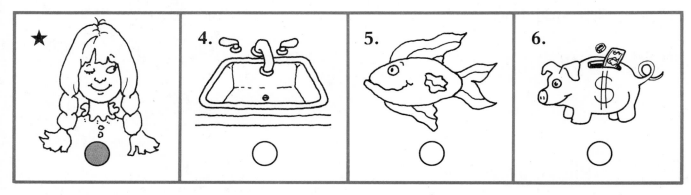

Fill in the circle next to the word that completes each sentence.

★ If you put that shirt in hot water, it will _____ .
   ○ sling   ● shrink   ○ string

7. Annie's favorite color is _____ .
   ○ trunk   ○ blink   ○ pink

8. We went the _____ way and got lost.
   ○ wring   ○ wrong   ○ wink

9. The _____ waved to the people from his tower.
   ○ king   ○ bank   ○ sting

Number right _____

Phonics Home Activity: Have your child tell which picture names in the first section have the sounds for *ng* and which pictures in the second section have the sounds for *nk*. Then ask your child to read the completed sentences at the bottom of the page.

Say the picture name in each box. Print the letters
that stand for the beginning sounds.

clown

plant

crown

princess

slide

spot

_____ ab

_____ oon

_____ ane

_____ ib

_____ aws

_____ ate

_____ acks

_____ ider

_____ ed

_____ ize

_____ ock

_____ ice

Read the sentences and look at the pictures. Print **A** next to the sentence that tells about Picture **A**. Print **B** next to the sentence that tells about Picture **B**.

A.  **B.**

He is <u>creeping</u> on the floor. _B_

He is <u>sweeping</u> the floor. _A_

Mom will wash the <u>grapes</u>. _____

Mom will wash the <u>drapes</u>. _____

 **A.**  **B.**

There's a <u>spider</u> on the rock. _____

There's a <u>sneaker</u> on the rock. _____

 **A.**  **B.**

The <u>smoke</u> is coming out. _____

The <u>skunk</u> is coming out. _____

 **A.**  **B.**

She will <u>clip</u> the cloth. _____

She will <u>press</u> the cloth. _____

 **A.**  **B.**

The <u>clerk</u> is in the store. _____

The <u>skirt</u> is in the store. _____

 **A.**  **B.**

84

Phonics Home Activity: Ask your child to read each sentence and to point to the picture he or she chose. Then, on another sheet of paper, help your child write the words *grape, smoke,* and *clip* without looking at them.

Circle the word that completes each sentence.
Then print the word.

1. A _____trout_____ is a kind of fish.

   stout   (trout)   scout

2. I eat my soup with a _____ .

   spool   spoke   spoon

3. There is a high _____ above the river.

   cliff   stiff   claws

4. We ate a _____ of cheese and fruit.

   snail   snack   crack

5. We saw _____ coming from a fire.

   choke   spoke   smoke

6. The final _____ of the game was 21-14.

   chore   score   snore

7. We saw a sudden _____ of light.

   flash   smash   crash

8. Alex is wearing a _____ coat.

   clay   gray   tray

Say each picture name. Fill in the circle next to the letters that stand for the beginning sounds.

★
- ○ sl
- ○ tr
- ● st

1.
- ○ pr
- ○ pl
- ○ gr

2.
- ○ bl
- ○ cl
- ○ cr

3.
- ○ sw
- ○ sl
- ○ sn

4.
- ○ st
- ○ dr
- ○ tr

5.
- ○ sm
- ○ sk
- ○ st

6.
- ○ sc
- ○ cl
- ○ sm

7.
- ○ dr
- ○ pr
- ○ br

Fill in the circle next to the word that completes each sentence.

★ The _____ got ready to fly the plane.
- ○ crate
- ○ flew
- ● crew

8. Amy is in the second _____ at school.
- ○ trade
- ○ blade
- ○ grade

9. The fresh orange juice was _____ and good.
- ○ sleet
- ○ sweet
- ○ great

10. Would you like a _____ of water?
- ○ blink
- ○ brick
- ○ drink

11. A _____ is a black and white animal.
- ○ skunk
- ○ trunk
- ○ spoke

Number right _____ ©

Houghton Mifflin Company. All rights reserved.

Phonics Home Activity: Have your child name the pictures on this page and tell which letters stand for the beginning sounds. Then ask your child to read the completed sentences at the bottom of the page. Help your child list things in your home whose names begin with the sounds for *sl, tr, st, sm,* and *cl.*

Say the picture name in each box. Print the
letters that stand for the beginning sound.

<u>scr</u>apbook    <u>spr</u>ing

<u>str</u>awberry    <u>thr</u>ee

 <u>scr</u>ewdriver	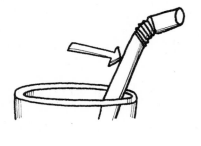 aw	 een
 ead	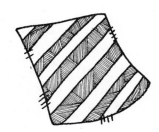 ipes	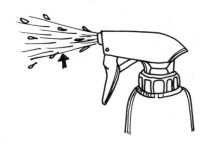 ay
 oller	 one	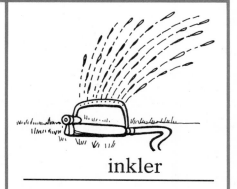 inkler

Print the word that completes each sentence.

spread   thrown   stream

Alex is having fun.

He is by the _____stream_____ .

He has just _____thrown_____ the fishing line.

throat   screwdriver   stroller

Jessie is helping her mother.

She is fixing the baby's _____ .

She is using a _____ .

thread   scraps   stretch

Ana is making something nice.

She is using _____ of cloth.

She is sewing them with _____ .

scream   throat   sprain

Poor Nicholas!

He has a _____ in his arm.

His _____ hurts, too.

Phonics Home Activity: Ask your child to read the completed sentences and explain how each picture helped in choosing which words to write. Then help your child look in a newspaper or magazine and circle pictures of things whose names begin with the sounds for *str, thr, scr,* and *spr.*

Read each meaning. Find the word in the box that goes with the meaning. Then print the word.

| spring | throat | strong | scribble | stretch |

1. To write very fast ___scribble___

2. The time after winter _____

3. To make longer by pulling _____

4. Part of the body _____

5. Able to lift heavy things _____

| scrambled | throne | thread | screen | spread |

6. Something to sit on ___throne___

7. What you look at to watch TV _____

8. Used for sewing _____

9. Often found on a bed _____

10. One way to eat eggs _____

Name _____

check

Say each picture name. Fill in the circle next to the letters that stand for the beginning sounds.

★	1.	2.	3.
○ spr ● scr ○ str	○ str ○ thr ○ scr	○ scr ○ str ○ thr	○ scr ○ str ○ spr

4.	5.	6.	7.
○ thr ○ spr ○ scr	○ spr ○ thr ○ str	○ scr ○ spr ○ thr	○ thr ○ spr ○ str

Fill in the circle next to the word that completes each sentence.

★ A _____ is someone you don't know.
    ● stranger   ○ spray   ○ screech

8. Winning the big game was a real _____ .
    ○ strip   ○ thrill   ○ screen

9. Robert will turn on the _____ in the garden.
    ○ sprinkler   ○ thread   ○ scrape

10. Our cat is gentle and will not _____ you.
    ○ strict   ○ scratch   ○ strap

11. My shirt has green and white _____ .
    ○ springs   ○ throne   ○ stripes   Number right _____

Phonics Home Activity: Have your child read the completed sentences at the bottom of the page. Then help your child cut out all the pictures in the top section. On another sheet of paper, have your child print *spr, scr,* and *thr* and paste the pictures under the correct heading.

Say the name of the picture in each box. Print the
letters that stand for the beginning sound.

cheese   photo   sheep   thermos

p̲h̲onograph   ___ip   ___erry   ___irteen

Print the letters that stand for the ending sound.

peac̲h̲   fis̲h̲   teet̲h̲   duc̲k̲

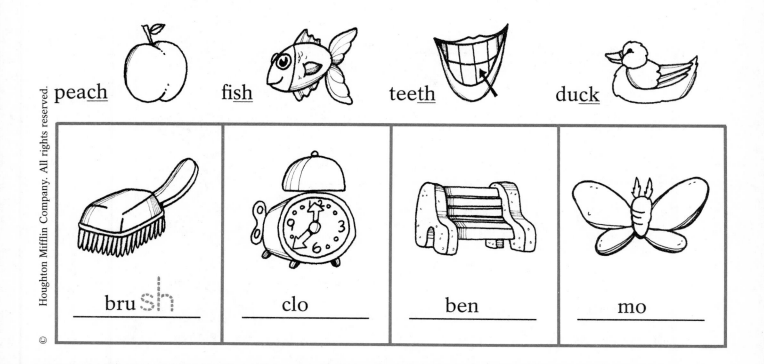

bru s̲h̲   clo___   ben___   mo___

Name _____   91

Circle the word that completes each sentence.
Then print the word.

1. Ben is a good __photographer__ .

microphone   (photographer)   thermometer

2. Beth is _____ .

chilly   thirsty   photo

3. Sam is looking at a _____ .
sharp   crack   chart

4. Here is a _____ problem.
mash   math   munch

5. Linda put out the _____ .
trash   chill   tuck

6. That is a good _____ .
truth   slick   trick

Phonics Home Activity: Ask your child to read the completed sentences on this page. Then, on another
sheet of paper, help your child list words that rhyme with *chart* (cart, smart, part) and words that rhyme with
trick (sick, stick, pick).

Read this story. Decide which word in the box makes sense in each space. Then print the word in the space.

luck	grandchild	phonograph	brush
theater	month	rushed	peach

"I want to do something special for Grandma," said Sara. "Her birthday is next _____month_____."

"Maybe you could give her tickets to the _____ for that new show," said Sam. "Or you could get her a new record to play on her _____."

"I don't have much money," said Sara. "I wish I did. Wait! I have an idea. Grandma has always loved the_____ tree in our yard. I'll paint a picture of that tree for her."

Sara got out her paints and _____.

"Great idea," said Sam. "Good _____!"

On her grandmother's birthday, Sara _____ over to her house with the picture.

Grandma was delighted. She said, "Sara, you're the best _____ in the world!"

Name _____   93

Say each picture name. Fill in the circle next to the letters that stand for the beginning sound.

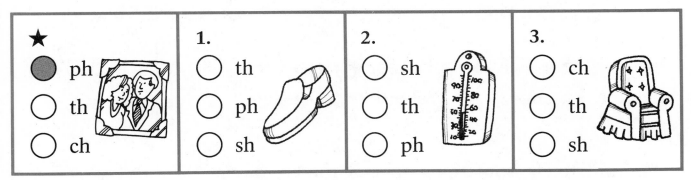

★
- ● ph
- ○ th
- ○ ch

1.
- ○ th
- ○ ph
- ○ sh

2.
- ○ sh
- ○ th
- ○ ph

3.
- ○ ch
- ○ th
- ○ sh

Say each picture name. Fill in the circle next to the letters that stand for the ending sound.

★
- ○ sh
- ● ch
- ○ ck

4.
- ○ sh
- ○ th
- ○ ck

5.
- ○ sh
- ○ th
- ○ ch

6.
- ○ sh
- ○ ph
- ○ ch

Fill in the circle next to the word that completes each sentence.

★ Nate helps his dad with _____ on the farm.
- ○ trophy
- ● chores
- ○ shores

7. We walk our dog on a _____.
- ○ leash
- ○ peach
- ○ thorn

8. There is a _____ tree in our yard.
- ○ leash
- ○ reach
- ○ peach

9. The book fell to the floor with a _____.
- ○ champ
- ○ thump
- ○ tooth

Number right _____

Phonics Home Activity: Divide a sheet of paper into four columns. Write the letters *ph, sh, ch,* and *th* as column heads. Help your child cut out the pictures. If a picture begins or ends with the sound at the top of a column, have the child paste the picture in that column.

Say the name of the picture in each box. Print the letter or letters that stand for the vowel sound.

c a t

b e d

g a t e

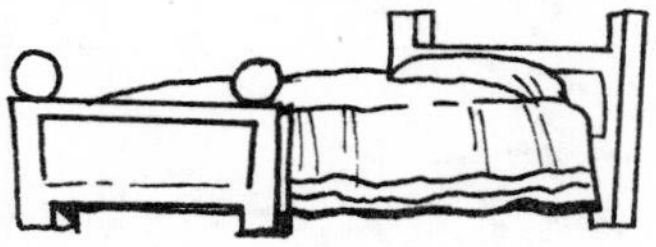

j e e p

 p a st e	 b ____ ll	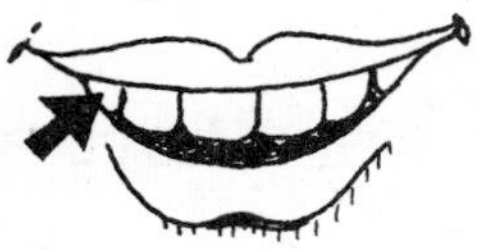 t _____ th	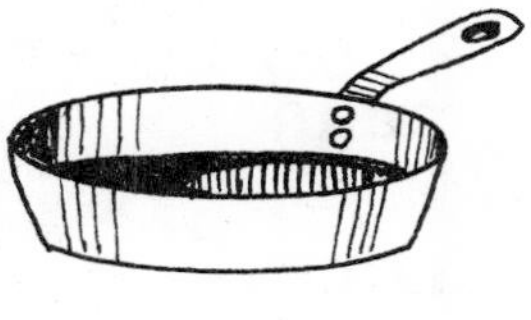 p ____ n
 f _____ t	 w ____ b	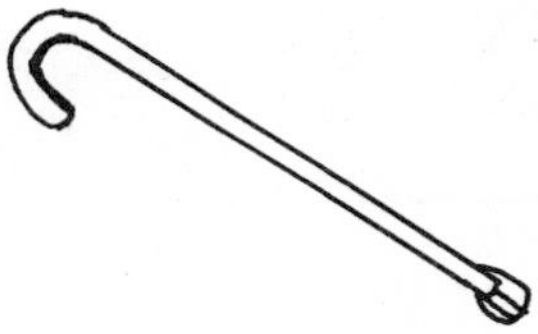 c ____ n ____	 sh _____ p
 fl ____ g	 t ____ p ____	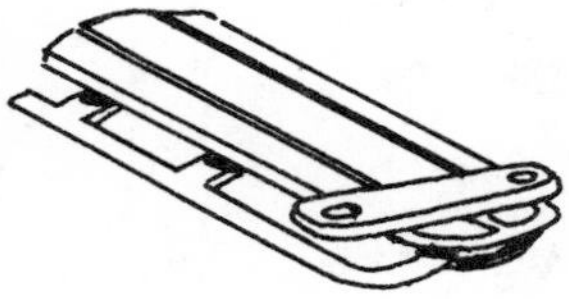 sl ____ d	 l ____ mp
 t ____ ck	 n ____ ck	 qu _____ n	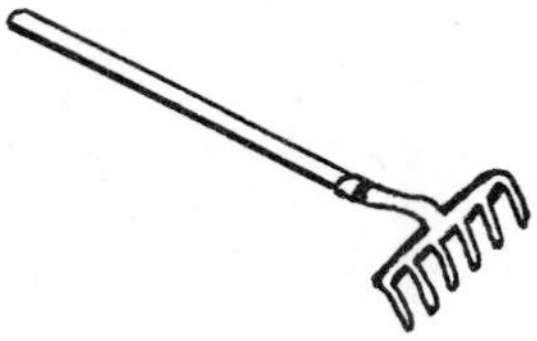 r ____ k ____

Name _____

Read the words in each box. Print each word under the heading that names the vowel sound in that word.

sand

bake

plane

man

make

name

hand

flat

Short a   **Long a**

sand

_____   _____

_____   _____

_____   _____

ten

week

sleep

set

leg

wheel

bed

seed

Short e   **Long e**

_____   _____

_____   _____

_____   _____

Phonics Home Activity: Have your child read the words he or she has written under each vowel-sound heading (short *a*, long *a*, short *e*, long *e*). Then, on another sheet of paper, help your child write a few of these words without looking at them.

Read each pair of sentences and look at the picture. Decide which word in the box completes the second sentence. Then print the word in the sentence.

cane	plane	step	cape
beet	pan	check	mane

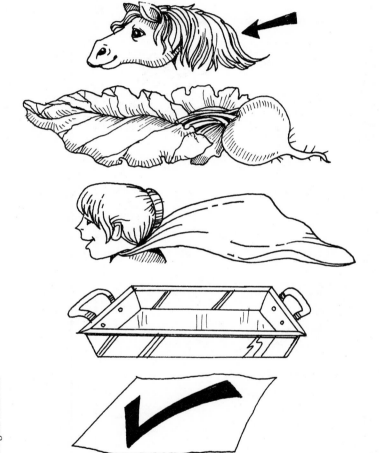

1. This isn't a <u>man</u>.
   It's a _____mane_____ .

2. This isn't a <u>bet</u>.
   It's a _____ .

3. This isn't a <u>cap</u>.
   It's a _____ .

4. This isn't a <u>pane</u>.
   It's a _____ .

5. This isn't a <u>cheek</u>.
   It's a _____ .

6. This isn't a <u>plan</u>.
   It's a _____ .

7. This isn't a <u>can</u>.
   It's a _____ .

Name _____

Say each picture name. Fill in the circle next to the word that names the picture.

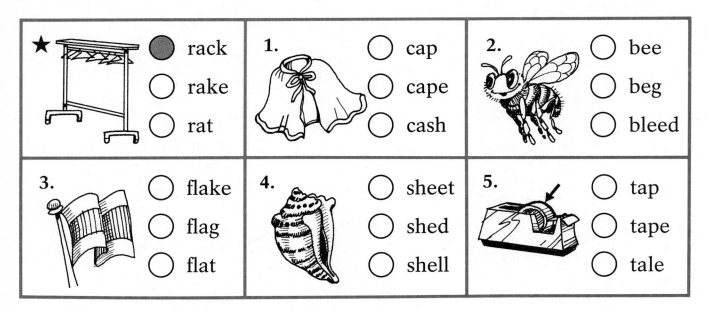

★ ● rack
  ○ rake
  ○ rat

1. ○ cap
   ○ cape
   ○ cash

2. ○ bee
   ○ beg
   ○ bleed

3. ○ flake
   ○ flag
   ○ flat

4. ○ sheet
   ○ shed
   ○ shell

5. ○ tap
   ○ tape
   ○ tale

Fill in the circle next to the word that completes each sentence.

★ Pet dogs are very _____.
  ● tame   ○ tap   ○ teeth

6. Mom is pulling _____ out of the garden.
   ○ weds   ○ weeds   ○ sweet

7. We use the _____ when it is hot.
   ○ flash   ○ fake   ○ fan

8. My dad _____ me at the bus stop.
   ○ met   ○ map   ○ mat

9. We live in a house by the _____.
   ○ lack   ○ lake   ○ late

Number right _____ ©

98 **Phonics Home Activity:** Have your child name the pictures in the top section and tell whether they contain the long *a* or *e* sound, or the short *a* or *e* sound. Then ask your child to read the sentences on the bottom section of the page.

Say the name of the picture in each box. Print the
letter or letters that stand for the vowel sound.

f<u>i</u>sh  k<u>i</u>t<u>e</u>  b<u>o</u>x

r<u>o</u>p<u>e</u>  b<u>u</u>s  m<u>u</u>l<u>e</u>

thr ⬭ n ⬭   dr ___ m   cl ___ ck   m ___ l ___

p ___ p ___   b ___ n ___   cr ___ b   b ___ s

m ___ lk   d ___ m ___   c ___ b ___   d ___ ll

Name _____   99

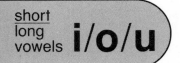

Read the words in each box. Print each word
under the heading that names the vowel sound in
that word.

| mile |
| hit |
| pig |
| drive |
| fine |
| list |

Short i   **Long i**

hit   mile

_____   _____

_____   _____

_____   _____

| got |
| stone |
| note |
| not |
| those |
| rock |

Short o   **Long o**

_____   _____

_____   _____

_____   _____

| truck |
| cute |
| cut |
| huge |
| cub |

Short u   **Long u**

_____   _____

_____   _____

_____   _____

Phonics Home Activity: Ask your child to read the words he or she has written under each vowel-sound
heading (short *i*, long *i*, short *o*, long *o*). Then, on another sheet of paper, help your child write a few sentences
that contain any two of these words. (For example, the *cub* is *cute*.)

Find the word that completes each sentence.
Then print the word in the sentence.

mop   mope   stove

Linda is cleaning the kitchen.

She is using a _____mop_____.

Then she will scrub the _____stove_____.

dish   dime   dim

Joan is at a yard sale.

She is buying a _____.

It costs a _____.

mule   mug   mud

Jed is having a hard time!

He fell into the _____.

The _____ is running away.

cone   cob   bone

Tim and his dog are outside.

Tim has corn on the _____.

His dog has a _____.

Name _____

check Say each picture name. Fill in the circle next to the word that names the picture.

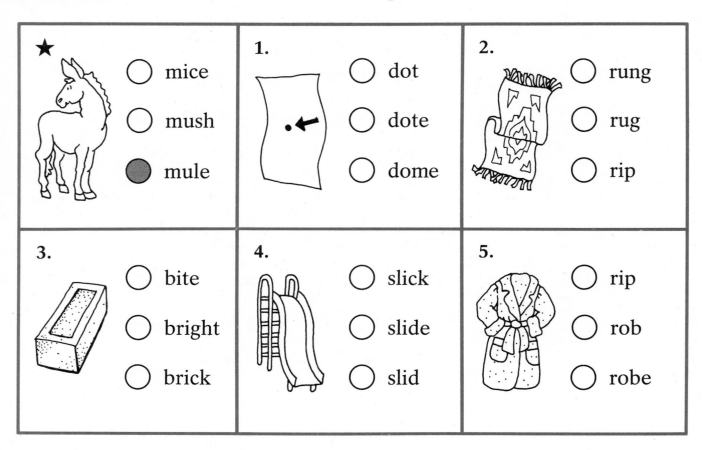

★
○ mice
○ mush
● mule

1.
○ dot
○ dote
○ dome

2.
○ rung
○ rug
○ rip

3.
○ bite
○ bright
○ brick

4.
○ slick
○ slide
○ slid

5.
○ rip
○ rob
○ robe

Fill in the circle next to the word that completes each sentence.

★ Can you tie a ＿＿＿ in this rope?
　○ knock　　● knot　　○ note

6. The king sat on the ＿＿＿ .
　○ throb　　○ throne　　○ thud

7. The fruit is not ＿＿＿ yet.
　○ rip　　○ ripe　　○ rug

8. Please push the baby on the ＿＿＿ .
　○ sweep　　○ swing　　○ wing

Number right ＿＿＿

Phonics Home Activity: Have your child name each picture and point to the correct word in each box. Then have your child read the completed sentences at the bottom of the page.

Say each picture name. Then print the letters that stand for the vowel sound in that name.

jeep   p<u>ai</u>nt

ch <u>ee</u> k   sn ____ l   qu ____ n   n ____ l

Print the letters that stand for the vowel sound in each picture name.

h<u>ay</u>   c<u>oa</u>t

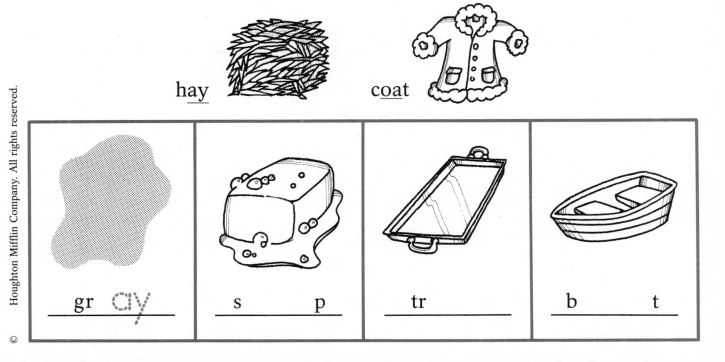

gr <u>ay</u>   s ____ p   tr ____   b ____ t

Name _____   **103**

vowel pairs review

Read each pair of sentences and look at the picture. Decide which word in the box completes the second sentence. Then print the word in the sentence.

chain	soap	tray	peel
toast	geese	mail	bee

1. This isn't the <u>mule</u>.

   It's the _____mail_____ .

2. This isn't a <u>bay</u>.

   It's a _____ .

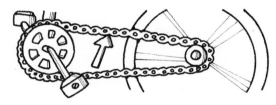

3. This isn't a <u>chin</u>.

   It's a _____ .

4. These are not <u>goats</u>.

   They are _____ .

5. This isn't a <u>test</u>.

   It's a piece of _____ .

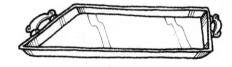

6. This isn't a <u>tree</u>.

   It's a _____ .

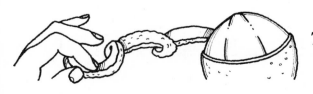

7. This isn't the orange <u>pail</u>.

   It's the orange _____ .

104 **Phonics Home Activity:** Ask your child to read each pair of sentences he or she completed on this page. Then have your child circle the letters that stand for the vowel sound in each word he or she wrote.

Read this story. Decide which word in the box makes sense in each space. Then print the word in the space.

creek	bait	free	fourteen
gray	oak	seen	loaf

Fay was staying with her grandfather. They had had rain and a ___gray___ sky every day. Today, at last, the sun was shining.

"Let's go fishing, Grandpa," said Fay. "I've just found some worms we can use as _____."

"Good," said Grandpa. "Let's take some cheese and a _____ of bread with us, too."

They walked down to the water and put their things under an _____ tree.

"There's a lot of water in the _____," said Fay. "I've never _____ it so high."

"That's because of all the rain we've had," said Grandpa. "The fishing should be good. Let's start."

Later, Fay said, "Grandpa! We've already caught _____ fish! That's enough for several _____ suppers for us!"

©

Name _____ 105

vowel pairs review

Circle the picture the sentence tells about. Then print the underlined word.

br<u>ea</u>d    b<u>ea</u>ch

1. Here is your <u>meal</u>.

___meal___

2. I will use the <u>thread</u>.

_____

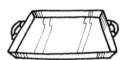 

3. This is a big <u>beak</u>.

_____

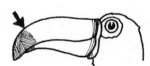  

Now complete these sentences. Circle the word you would use. Then print it.

1. The word <u>thread</u> has the same vowel sound as ___bread___ .

   (bread)   beach

2. The word <u>grease</u> has the same vowel sound as _____ .

   bread   beach

 Houghton Mifflin Company. All rights reserved. © **Phonics Home Activity:** Have your child read each sentence in the top section of this page and point to the picture it tells about. Then ask your child to read the completed sentences at the bottom of the page.

Read each meaning. Find the word in the box that goes with the meaning. Then print the word.

thread	feathers	peach	weak

1. Opposite of *strong* _____weak_____

2. A kind of fruit _____

3. Something birds have _____

4. Something to sew with _____

sweater	seal	beans	wealth	dead

5. An animal _____

6. Not living _____

7. Something to wear _____

8. A kind of vegetable _____

© 9. A lot of money _____

Name _____

check

Say each picture name. Fill in the circle next to the word that names the picture.

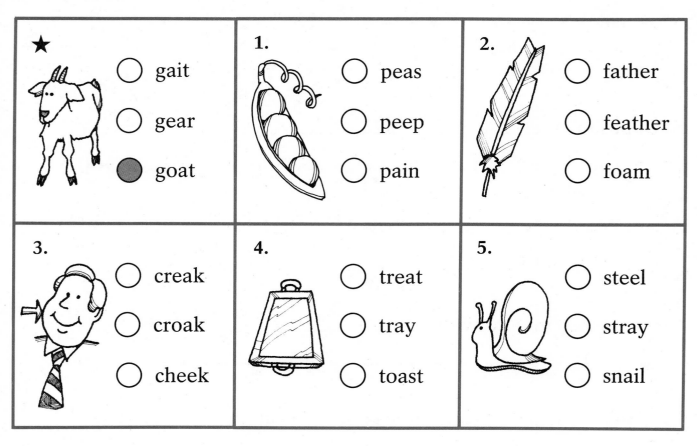

★
- ○ gait
- ○ gear
- ● goat

1.
- ○ peas
- ○ peep
- ○ pain

2.
- ○ father
- ○ feather
- ○ foam

3.
- ○ creak
- ○ croak
- ○ cheek

4.
- ○ treat
- ○ tray
- ○ toast

5.
- ○ steel
- ○ stray
- ○ snail

Fill in the circle next to the word that completes each sentence.

★ Cows give us milk and _____ .
○ creep   ● cream   ○ croak

6. She ordered a _____ hamburger with nothing on it.
○ plead   ○ plain   ○ peace

7. Please _____ the butter on the bread.
○ speed   ○ scream   ○ spread

8. We all got _____ from the rain.
○ soaked   ○ seek   ○ sway

Number right _____ ©

Phonics Home Activity: Ask your child to name each picture in the top section of this page and to tell which vowel pair the picture name contains. Then have your child read the completed sentences and choose two of them to copy and illustrate on a separate sheet of paper.

Find the word in the box that belongs in each
sentence. Then print the word.

belt	met	tape	pot	lid	slide

1. On the playground, we like the ____slide____ best.

2. We listened to a _____ of good music.

3. We made soup in a _____ .

4. To open the jar, turn the _____ .

5. I _____ my friends in the park.

6. Norma is wearing a pretty red _____ .

Now use the words you just wrote in this puzzle.
Write each word next to the number of the
sentence it is in.

Name _____   **109**

Here are some riddles. The answers are in the box below. Find the answer to each riddle and print it on the line.

a joke	a mule	your lap	the sun
a quilt	a bed	five	a plane

1. What has legs but cannot walk?

   _____a bed_____

2. What is not a bird but can still fly?

   _____

3. What never sleeps but stays on a bed?

   _____

4. What is told just to make us laugh?

   _____

5. What animal works very hard for us?

   _____

6. If a boy is four, what will he soon be?

   _____

7. What gives us light that we never have to pay for?

   _____

Phonics Home Activity: Have your child read and answer each riddle. Then ask your child to choose two of the riddles to copy and illustrate on another sheet of paper. Illustrations may be as imaginative as your child wishes.

What Animal Can You Find?

Find an animal that can really kick!

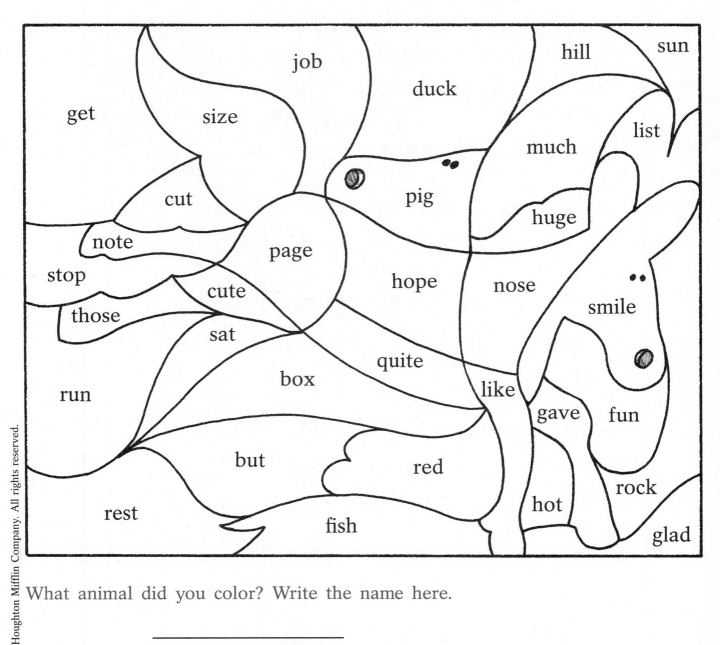

Read the word in each shape. If the word has a
short vowel sound, color the shape green. If the
word has a long vowel sound, color the shape brown.

job

duck

hill   sun

get   size

much   list

cut

pig

note   page   huge

stop   cute   hope   nose

those

smile

sat

run   quite

box   like

but   red   gave   fun

rest   fish   hot   rock

glad

What animal did you color? Write the name here.

_____

pig   mole   mule

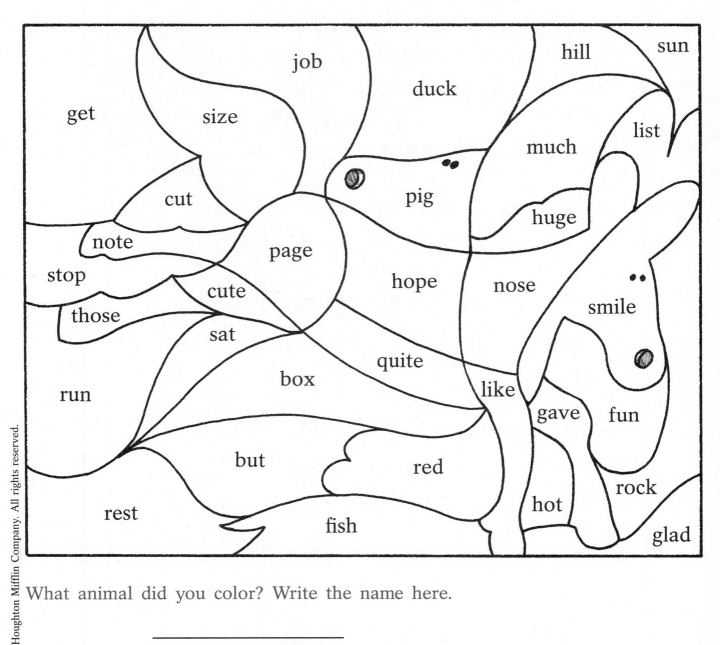

Name _____

Read this story.

Kate and Jon went for a ride on a bike made for two. Kate was in front. Jon was in back.

At first, they rode on flat land. They found that two people on one bike can go quite fast.

"This is fun!" yelled Kate. But Jon wasn't so sure. This ride was a bit *too* fast for him.

Then they rode up a big hill. It was hard work! They huffed and puffed all the way up. At the top, they got off the bike to rest.

"I didn't think we were going to make it," Kate gasped. "I was ready to quit."

"So was I," said Jon. "If I hadn't kept the brake on, we would have rolled back down!"

Circle the word that completes each sentence. Then print the word.

back
(bike)
band

rod
rode
ran

brake
bike
gasp

1. Kate and Jon went on a _____bike_____.

2. Then they _____ up a big hill.

3. Jon had kept the _____ on

while they went up the hill.

Phonics Home Activity: Ask your child to read the story in the top section and the completed sentences at the bottom of the page. Then help your child write the words *bike, bark, rode, rod,* and *brake* without looking at them.

Read each sentence and decide what the underlined word is. Then find the word in the letter boxes below the sentences. Color those letter boxes to make the word stand out. Use yellow or some other light color.

1. We read a story about a huge, scary <u>giant</u>.
2. She held her bag by the <u>strap</u>.
3. The teacher gave a <u>quiz</u> on what we just read.
4. It was a <u>thrill</u> to meet my favorite singer.
5. There is a big <u>bridge</u> over the water.
6. My big brother is on the football <u>squad</u>.
7. Let's <u>sprinkle</u> some water on the garden.
8. She was on the <u>stage</u> when she sang her song.

R	O	M	S	P	R	I	N	K	L	E	N
O	B	R	I	D	G	E	P	A	G	E	K
T	H	I	S	S	Q	U	A	D	A	N	D
A	T	G	I	A	N	T	O	P	O	N	Y
G	A	T	E	T	H	R	I	L	L	G	O
R	S	T	A	G	E	C	S	P	R	A	Y
T	H	R	O	A	T	X	S	T	R	A	P
S	Q	U	I	D	L	Q	U	I	Z	N	O

Now see how many *other* words you can find in this puzzle!

Name _____ 113

Find the word in the box that belongs in each sentence. Print the word.

sprinkler	strawberry	square
thread	giraffe	queen

1. A _____square_____ has four sides.

2. We turned on the water in the _____ .

3. I ate a big red _____ .

4. I used _____ to fix a hole in my shirt.

5. That woman is the _____ .

6. A _____ is an animal in our zoo.

Help the zookeeper find the lost animal!

Start with the zookeeper. Find the picture of each word you just wrote. Draw a line from one picture to the next, in order, until you come to the lost animal.

Phonics Home Activity: Ask your child to read each completed sentence and point to the picture in the maze that illustrates the word he or she wrote. Then help your child name the other pictures in the maze and tell what letter or letters stand for the beginning sound in each of those picture names.

A word that contains a vowel followed by *r* or *re* is hiding in the letters beside each number. A clue to that word is given below the letters.

Find the word and circle it. Then print the letters of the word in the boxes.

1. G N B A R N A P

   A place where animals are kept

2. O B U R N F O U

   What fire does

3. M O P U R R F E

   What cats do

   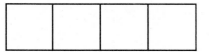

4. H A R E L E B B

   A rabbit-like animal

   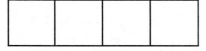

5. A M W H I R L P

   To turn around and around

   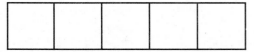

6. E P E R H I R E

   To pay someone to work for you

   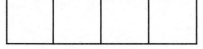

7. H I S O R E L W

   How you may feel after you fall

   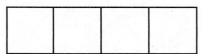

©

Name _____

Find the word in the box that belongs in each
sentence. Print the word.

tore	fern	horse
art	pure	spare

1. A _____horse_____ is an animal.

2. Drawings and paintings are two kinds of _____ .

3. A _____ is a kind of plant.

4. Seth _____ the paper into two pieces.

5. When we had a flat tire, we put on the _____ .

6. The dirty water is not _____ .

Now use the words you just wrote in this puzzle.
Write each word next to the number of the
sentence it is in.

Phonics Home Activity: Ask your child to read the completed sentences on this page and then show where
each word belongs in the crossword puzzle. Then have your child list things in your home that contain the
sounds for *or, er,* and *ar.*

Here are some riddles. The answers are in the box below. Find the answer to each riddle and print it on the line.

1. What do you need to get on the bus?

   the fare

2. What can make you sick?

   _____

3. What do you get if you add six and seven?

   _____

4. What has four sides all alike?

   _____

5. What is black and is put on streets?

   _____

6. What helps you to eat your dinner?

   _____

7. What probably scares a shark?

   _____

8. Who is the most picked-on person at a baseball game?

   _____

tar

germs

a larger
shark

a fork

the umpire

a square

thirteen

the fare

Name _____

review

Read this story.

There once was a rich man who bought
a large gold piece. He put it into a hole
and covered it up with dirt. Each day, he would
dig up the gold just to admire it. One day,
a stranger saw the man do this. The stranger
returned after dark and took the gold.

The next day, a servant heard the rich man
cry out. She ran to see what was the matter.

"My gold is gone!" moaned the rich man.

The servant said, "Don't let it bother you,
sir. I caught the man and got the gold piece
back."

"Oh, thank you!" the rich man said.
"Please take the gold piece as a gift."

Circle the word that completes each sentence.
Then print the word.

	dirt
	cover
1. The man had a 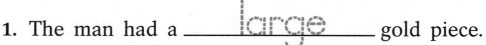large_____ gold piece.	(large)
	dark

	dirt
2. He covered the gold with _____ .	admire
	dark

| | cover |
| 3. A _____ took the gold. | stranger |

Read each sentence. Decide what the underlined word is.

1. A bird <u>flies</u> through the air.
2. Tom's dad is our fire <u>chief</u>.
3. Do you want your potato baked or <u>fried</u>?
4. It's a <u>relief</u> to go for a swim on a hot day.
5. Lana is Mr. Blake's <u>niece</u>.
6. My wet shoes <u>dried</u> in the sun.
7. Corn and wheat were growing in the <u>field</u>.
8. Ted is going to <u>lie</u> down and rest.

The underlined words you just read are in the puzzle below. Read the word in each shape. If *ie* stands for the long *i* sound, color the shape blue. If *ie* stands for the long *e* sound, color the shape yellow. Find out what Mr. Blue wears to work!

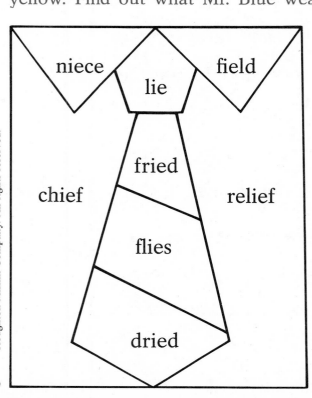

Now complete this sentence.

Mr. Blue wears a

blue _____.

shirt   pin   tie

Name _____

Read this story. Decide which word in the box belongs in each space. Then print the word in the space.

movie	spies	thief	tried
died	collie	cried	brief

Almost all of us like to see a ___movie___ once in a while. People have been going to movies for a long time. Many of us have laughed at the funny movies and have _____ at the sad ones.

There are all kinds of movies. Some are long, but others are _____ . There are movies about all kinds of people. You might see a movie about a _____ who takes something and later gets caught. There are many movies about people such as detectives, secret agents, and _____ .

Some movies are about animals. One animal in movies that many people still remember was a dog named Lassie. Lassie was a special dog called a _____ . In her movies, Lassie always _____ to do right, and she often saved people's lives. Long after Lassie had _____ , people were able to remember her by seeing her old movies.

Phonics Home Activity: Ask your child to read the whole story, inserting the words in the sentences he or she completed. Then have your child select one or more sentences from the story to copy and illustrate on another sheet of paper.

120

Read this story.

Kim <u>Choy</u> had been the new girl at school last week. Now it was the weekend. Kim felt alone.

"Don't be sad, Kim," said her mother. "You'll make friends soon." Kim tried to be cheerful. She helped her father change the <u>oil</u> in the car. Then she and her mother started to make <u>oyster</u> soup.

Suddenly Kim heard <u>voices</u> outside. She went to the window and saw some <u>boys</u> and girls from her class playing ball across the street.

One boy looked over and saw Kim. He waved to her and shouted, "Kim! Come and <u>join</u> us!"

Kim smiled with <u>joy</u>. Her mother said, "The oyster soup can wait. Go <u>enjoy</u> your new friends!"

Circle the word that completes each sentence. Then print the word.

voices
oil
oysters
joy
noise

1. Kim heard children's _____voices_____ outside.

2. A boy asked Kim to _____ them.

join
oil
oyster
voice

3. Mother said, "The _____ soup can wait."

Name _____

A word that contains *oi* or *oy* is hiding in the letters beside each number. A clue to that word is given below the letters.

Find the word and circle it. Then print the letters of the word in the boxes.

1. E R J O I N O T

   To get into a club

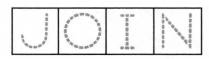

2. H I S O I L A P

   What plants grow in

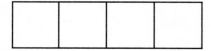

3. B I B O Y S E E

   Children who are not girls

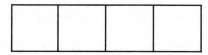

4. A R C O I N O T

   One kind of money

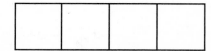

5. S L O J O Y E S

   A feeling when you're happy

6. I G O I L E F T

   Used in a car

7. L E T O Y A R D

   Something to play with

122 **Phonics Home Activity:** Ask your child to read each riddle and the answer that is written in the boxes. Then have your child cut out each answer and paste it on a separate sheet of paper under the heading *oi* or *oy*.

Read each sentence and decide what the underlined word is. Then find the word in the letter boxes below the sentences. Color those letter boxes to make the word stand out. Use yellow or some other light color.

1. There's a <u>slight</u> chance that the Bears will win.
2. We can <u>bind</u> the papers together with string.
3. The sunset was a beautiful <u>sight</u>.
4. I <u>wind</u> my watch once a day.
5. We saw the birds in <u>flight</u>.
6. They will <u>grind</u> the wheat at the mill.
7. The light was very <u>bright</u>.
8. We took the <u>rind</u> off the orange.

C	O	R	N	I	B	S	I	G	H	T	Y
O	Y	E	S	S	L	I	G	H	T	R	C
U	G	R	I	N	D	T	O	B	O	Y	S
T	O	A	S	T	F	O	X	R	I	N	D
L	O	G	B	I	N	D	N	O	I	S	E
O	B	R	I	G	H	T	Z	H	I	G	H
S	T	A	M	P	I	N	S	W	I	N	D
O	N	F	L	I	G	H	T	V	P	E	N

Now see how many *other* words you can find in this puzzle!

©

Name _____

Read this story. Decide which word in the box belongs in each space.

| flight | brightly | | mind |
| frightened | tightly | reminded | find |

Gabe had never been on an airplane before.

Today he was going on his first _____flight_____ .

"Don't lose your ticket, dear," his mother

_____ him. "And have a good time!"

Gabe got on the plane. A woman helped him to

_____ his seat by a window.

When the plane took off, Gabe closed his eyes

and held on _____ to the seat. Then he

turned and looked out the window.

There he was, above the clouds, with the sun

shining _____ in the sky. He looked

out the window for the rest of the time.

When the airplane landed, his friend Dwight was there.

"How did you like it?" asked Dwight.

"It was *great*," said Gabe. "I wasn't

_____ at all. I wouldn't _____

taking off again right now!"

Phonics Home Activity: Ask your child to read the completed story. Then, on another sheet of paper, help
124 your child write a few words that rhyme with *flight* (night, light, bright), and a few words that rhyme with *find*
(mind, kind, remind).

Say each picture name. Fill in the circle next to the word that names the picture.

★ ○ goose
   ● giraffe
   ○ ginger

1. ○ queen
   ○ strain
   ○ squeeze

2. ○ spread
   ○ squad
   ○ thread

3. ○ stream
   ○ seam
   ○ steam

4. ○ stake
   ○ stage
   ○ stag

5. ○ scare
   ○ stare
   ○ square

6. ○ spray
   ○ flaw
   ○ straw

7. ○ squat
   ○ quarter
   ○ throat

8. ○ troll
   ○ spruce
   ○ stroller

9. ○ bridge
   ○ bride
   ○ brief

10. ○ giant
    ○ germ
    ○ gorge

11. ○ kilt
    ○ quilt
    ○ wilt

12. ○ ripe
    ○ stripes
    ○ trips

13. ○ stray
    ○ spray
    ○ ray

14. ○ cane
    ○ cage
    ○ charge

©

Number right _____

Name _____ 125

Fill in the circle next to the word that completes each sentence.

★ We grew yellow and green _____ in our garden.
  ○ starch   ○ stretch   ● squash

1. The dancers are on the _____ .
   ○ stage   ○ slack   ○ stash

2. My _____ hurts from shouting at the game.
   ○ strict   ○ sprout   ○ throat

3. We will _____ water on the garden.
   ○ spray   ○ tray   ○ stray

4. We heard the little pigs _____ .
   ○ quack   ○ squeal   ○ quail

5. The teacher gave us a short _____ today.
   ○ whiz   ○ quiz   ○ fuzz

6. The baseball player wasn't happy when he _____ out.
   ○ quack   ○ struck   ○ pluck

7. We had to _____ playing when it got dark.
   ○ squint   ○ quit   ○ slit

8. The _____ will decide who wins the race.
   ○ jug   ○ jog   ○ judge

Number right _____ ©

126 **Phonics Home Activity:** Ask your child to read the completed sentences on this page. Then help your child write the words *stage, spray,* and *quit* without looking at them.

Say each picture name. Fill in the circle next to the word that names the picture.

★
○ chase
○ coil
● chief

1.
○ sore
○ soil
○ sort

2.
○ horn
○ harm
○ hammer

3.
○ tap
○ tape
○ tip

4.
○ pop
○ pip
○ pipe

5.
○ curl
○ circle
○ cord

6.
○ squirt
○ squire
○ square

7.
○ tray
○ tea
○ tie

8.
○ not
○ net
○ nut

9.
○ wire
○ wore
○ whirl

10.
○ mind
○ mop
○ mope

11.
○ terms
○ ties
○ toys

12.
○ knit
○ night
○ net

13
○ stir
○ stare
○ star

14.
○ pea
○ pie
○ pay

Number right _____

©

Name _____

Fill in the circle next to the word that completes each sentence.

★ If you pull that cloth, it will _____ .
   ● rip   ○ ripe   ○ rind

1. Jane ran _____ my house.
   ○ paste   ○ past   ○ poison

2. The fresh snow on the trees was a beautiful _____ .
   ○ sight   ○ sift   ○ sire

3. Our dog can stand up on its _____ legs.
   ○ hire   ○ hind   ○ hip

4. This monster story may _____ you.
   ○ rare   ○ scar   ○ scare

5. The _____ was caught when he tried to run away.
   ○ thirst   ○ thorn   ○ thief

6. The boys like to _____ water on each other.
   ○ square   ○ squirt   ○ squire

7. Sid was quiet, but his little brother was _____ .
   ○ royal   ○ niece   ○ noisy

8. My favorite color is _____ .
   ○ perch   ○ pried   ○ purple

9. Ellen _____ her new blue coat.
   ○ wore   ○ wind   ○ void

10. In a car, be sure to wear your seat _____ .
   ○ burn   ○ boil   ○ belt

Number right _____ ©

Phonics Home Activity: Ask your child to read the completed sentences on this page. Then have your child choose two of the sentences to copy and illustrate on another sheet of paper.

Find the word in the box that belongs in each sentence. Then print the word.

photos	alphabet	trophy
phone	phonograph	elephant

1. The winner held up his ___trophy___ .

2. My mom took _____ of our club.

3. Let's put a record on the _____ and dance.

4. My little sister is learning to say the _____ .

5. We saw a clown riding on the _____ at the zoo.

6. Phil's _____ is ringing.

Help Phil answer his call!

Find the picture of each word you just wrote. Then draw a line from one picture to the next, in order, until you come to the thing that is ringing.

Name _____

Here are some riddles. The answers are in the box below. Find the answer to each riddle and print it on the line.

1. What is an animal you can tell by its smell?

   _____a skunk_____

2. What do we use to breathe?

   _____

3. Where do many people put their money?

   _____

4. What is the opposite of *right*?

   _____

5. What can only a man be?

   _____

6. What comes before summer?

   _____

7. What can your mind do that your eyes can't?

   _____

8. If you mix red paint with white paint, what do you get?

   _____

wrong
a skunk
think
our lungs
in a bank
pink paint
a king
spring

Phonics Home Activity: Have your child read and answer each riddle. Then ask your child to choose two of the riddles to copy and illustrate on another sheet of paper. Illustrations may be as imaginative as your child wishes.

Clara and her friend like to write letters to each other. Read the letters.

Dear Britt,

    Guess what!

    It's supposed to be Spring and we still have snow at our house. The main roads are clear now, but our street is still slippery.

    I wish I could get on a plane and fly down there.

    Please write soon.

             Love,

             Clara

Dear Clara,

    If you come, bring your bathing suit! We can swim and play on the water slide.

    Our grass is always green, but our sky is not always blue! Yesterday there was a storm and the back yard was flooded.

    Try to write again soon.

             Love,

             Britt

Circle the word that completes each sentence. Then print the word.

sky
snow
swim

1. Clara said she still had _____ at her house.

slippery
blue
flooded

© **2.** Britt said her back yard was _____ .

Name _____

Find the word in the box that belongs in each sentence. Then print the word.

| thunder | photograph | shore | finish | chapter |

1. Nan likes to walk along the _____shore_____ at the beach.

2. Sharon will take a _____ of us.

3. My dog hides under the bed when it hears _____ .

4. I can't wait to read _____ three of this book.

5. I'll call you back when I _____ eating.

Now use the words you just wrote in this puzzle.
Write the word next to the number of the sentence it is in.

Phonics Home Activity: Have your child read the sentences he or she completed on this page and show where each word belongs in the crossword puzzle. Then ask your child to copy and illustrate a few of the words in the puzzle.

132

Jake has two nice pets named Oro and Goldy. They are easy to take care of. They don't eat much, and they never make noise.

Find out what kind of pets Oro and Goldy are. Read the word in each shape. If the word has a short vowel sound, color the shape orange. If the word has a long vowel sound, color the shape blue.

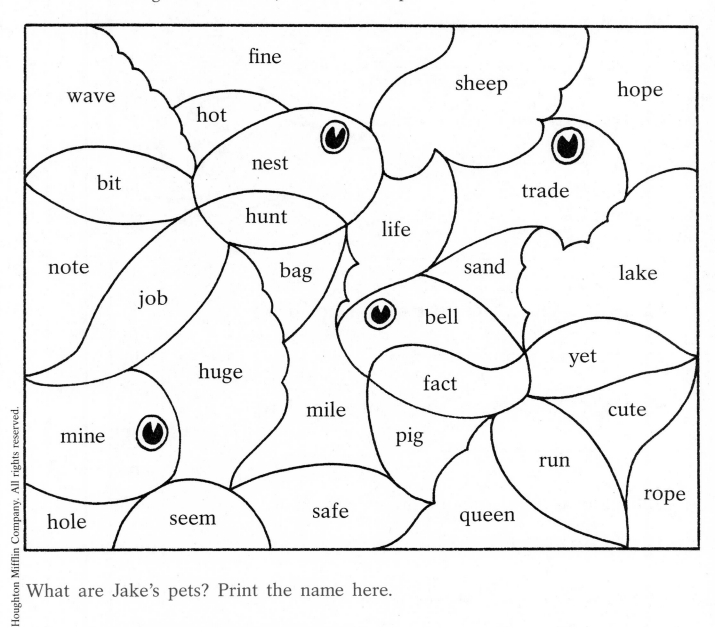

What are Jake's pets? Print the name here.

_____

pigs   mice   fish

©

Here are some riddles. The answers are in the box below. Find the answer to each riddle and print it on the line.

1. What plant likes to climb the walls?

   a vine

2. What is a group of sheep called?

   _____

3. What is an opening in a fence?

   _____

4. Where can a pot stay hot?

   _____

5. Where is a nice place to be on a hot day?

   _____

6. What can show you if you're early or late?

   _____

7. What gets walked on but doesn't seem to mind?

   _____

8. What keeps a lot of things together?

   _____

a clock
in the shade
a rug
a paper clip
a vine
on the stove
a gate
a flock

Phonics Home Activity: Have your child read and answer each riddle. Then, on another sheet of paper, help your child list words that rhyme with *gate* (late, skate, date), and words that rhyme with *flock* (lock, sock, clock).

Read each sentence and decide what the underlined word is. Then find the word in the letter boxes below the sentences. Color those letter boxes to make the word stand out. Use yellow or some other light color.

1. The baby often <u>wails</u> when she is hungry.
2. A <u>weed</u> is a plant most people don't want.
3. Jan's room is <u>neat</u>, but mine is a mess!
4. That bird is a blue <u>jay</u>.
5. The eye of the needle is too small for this <u>thread</u>.
6. At supper time, we had a special <u>treat</u>.
7. Dad made a <u>loaf</u> of bread today.

H	A	Y	T	R	E	A	T	H	E	A	D
T	H	R	E	A	D	Z	W	H	E	E	L
S	N	E	E	Z	E	B	C	L	E	A	N
S	A	Y	W	A	I	L	S	B	O	A	T
X	L	O	A	F	X	S	C	D	E	A	F
C	R	O	A	K	T	E	A	W	E	E	D
W	J	A	Y	C	P	A	I	N	T	E	R
N	E	A	T	D	F	G	R	E	A	T	J

Now see how many *other* words you can find in
© this puzzle!

Name _____ 135

Read this story. Decide which word in the box belongs in each space. Print the word in the space.

claims	meal	steep	peak
delay		goal	instead

A goat was eating grass high up on a mountain _____peak_____ . Far below, a lion saw him.

"That goat would make a fine dinner," the lion thought. "But I can't climb up there. The mountain is too _____ for me. I'll get the goat to come down here _____ ."

"Goat!" called the lion. "The grass tastes better down here. You'll get a better dinner. Come down now, without _____ !"

The goat didn't believe the lion. He said to himself, "The lion _____ that I'll get a better dinner down there. But the lion's real _____ is to have *me* for *his* dinner!"

So the goat called down, "No thanks, Lion! I won't be a _____ for *you* today!"

Phonics Home Activity: Have your child read the whole story, filling in each blank with the correct word. Then, on a separate sheet of paper, ask your child to copy and illustrate a few sentences from the story.

Say each picture name. Fill in the circle next to the word that names the picture.

★	○ drapes ● grapes ○ praise	**1.**	○ truck ○ trunk ○ track	**2.**	○ teach ○ teeth ○ tease
3.	○ wick ○ wig ○ wing	**4.**	○ shower ○ chowder ○ flower	**5.**	○ screen ○ stream ○ seen
6.	○ drag ○ flag ○ snag	**7.**	○ skunk ○ stack ○ slung	**8.**	○ stroke ○ smoke ○ spoke
9.	○ sing ○ cling ○ swing	**10.**	○ throne ○ phone ○ shone	**11.**	○ sail ○ snail ○ nail
12.	○ stock ○ croak ○ clock	**13.**	○ stale ○ scale ○ sale	**14.**	○ shin ○ thin ○ chin

Number right _____

Name _____

check

Fill in the circle next to the word that completes each sentence.

★ We play our records on our _____.

○ autograph ● phonograph ○ photocopy

1. When you see _____, you know there's a fire.

○ frames ○ blames ○ flames

2. Please write with care, and don't _____.

○ settle ○ scribble ○ thrill

3. We _____ our eyes often without even thinking about it.

○ slang ○ spank ○ blink

4. Dad came home and _____ up his coat.

○ hung ○ clung ○ hunk

5. Cindy has red hair and _____.

○ freckles ○ florist ○ bless

6. Dana keeps pictures of his friends in a _____.

○ stumble ○ scrapbook ○ smokestack

7. The old road is bumpy, but the new one is _____.

○ smooth ○ snoop ○ swoop

8. Mrs. Frank takes care of a _____ of sheep.

○ clock ○ shock ○ flock

Number right _____ ©

Phonics Home Activity: Ask your child to read a few of the sentences he or she has completed. Then help your child list things in your home whose names begin with the sounds for *fr, bl,* and *fl.*

138

Fill in the circle next to the word that names the
picture.

★	○ met ● meat ○ mat	1.	○ seep ○ seam ○ soap	2.	○ wag ○ wig ○ web
3.	○ cheap ○ chin ○ chain	4.	○ badge ○ brake ○ budge	5.	○ pay ○ pie ○ pea
6.	○ has ○ hose ○ his	7.	○ sail ○ sell ○ seal	8.	○ beet ○ bite ○ belt
9.	○ vest ○ vain ○ vase	10.	○ must ○ mice ○ meek	11.	○ cub ○ cube ○ crib
12.	○ scram ○ screen ○ scrape	13.	○ threw ○ throat ○ thread	14.	○ cat ○ kit ○ cot

©

Number right _____

Name _____

139

Fill in the circle next to the word that completes each sentence.

★ Kirk is carrying a heavy _____ of books.
- ◯ lead
- ● load
- ◯ lid

1. The fruit on the tree is almost _____ .
- ◯ rip
- ◯ ripe
- ◯ reap

2. Marcel was _____ because his train was late.
- ◯ drain
- ◯ delayed
- ◯ dipped

3. Shelly has a _____ sister.
- ◯ twin
- ◯ twine
- ◯ tweet

4. I cleaned the floor with a _____ .
- ◯ mope
- ◯ mump
- ◯ mop

5. Jane put on her green _____ .
- ◯ swell
- ◯ sweeter
- ◯ sweater

6. She tied the rope around her _____ .
- ◯ weak
- ◯ wink
- ◯ waist

7. It's time to _____ the meat.
- ◯ rod
- ◯ roast
- ◯ roost

8. The sky was _____ and cloudy.
- ◯ grab
- ◯ gray
- ◯ greet

9. We ate some fresh _____ .
- ◯ pain
- ◯ peas
- ◯ pried

Number right _____ ©

140 **Phonics Home Activity:** Ask your child to read the completed sentences on this page. Then help your child write the words *ripe*, *twin*, and *gray* without looking at them.

Sounds I Am Learning

Review	1	2	3	4	5	6
	7	8	9	10	**11**	**12**
Short Vowel Sounds (CVC)	13	14	15	16	17	18
	19	20	21	22	**23**	**24**
qu/squ	25	26	27	**28**		
g/j	29	30	31	**32**		
thr/str/spr	33	34	35	**36**		
Long Vowel Sounds (CVCe)	37	38	39	40	41	42
	43	44	**45**	**46**		
er/ir/ur	47	48	49	**50**		
ar	51	52	53	**54**		
or	55	56	57	**58**		
ie	59	60	61	**62**		
oi/oy	63	64	65	**66**		

© Name _____

★ The numbers on the chart are workbook page numbers.
  Light numbers are practice pages.
  Dark numbers are Check pages.

Vowel Plus **re**	67	68	69	**70**	
ind/ight	71	72	73	**74**	
ph	75	76	77	**78**	
ng/nk	79	80	81	**82**	
Consonant Review Two-letter Clusters	83	84	85	**86**	
Consonant Review Three-letter Clusters	87	88	89	**90**	
Consonant Review Digraphs	91	92	93	**94**	
Short/Long Vowels **a, e**	95	96	97	**98**	
Short/Long Vowels **i, o, u**	99	100	101	**102**	
Vowel Pairs Review	103	104	105	106	107 **108**
Review	109 110 111 112 113 114				
	115 116 117 118 119 120				
	121 122 123 124 **125 126**				
	127 128 129 130 131 132				
	133 134 135 136 **137 138**				
	139 140				

★ **The numbers on the chart are workbook page numbers.**
   Light numbers are practice pages.
   Dark numbers are Check pages.